INSTRUCTION

RELATING TO THE
PRINCIPLES OF

HEALTHFUL LIVING

COMPILED FROM THE
WRITINGS OF

MRS. ELLEN G. WHITE

THIRD EDITION — REVISED
THIRTEENTH THOUSAND

PUBLISHED BY THE
MEDICAL MISSIONARY BOARD
BATTLE CREEK, MICH.
1898.

Copyright © 1997 TEACH Services, Inc.

ISBN 0-945383-91-6
Library of Congress Catalog Card No. 96-61986

Published by

TEACH Services, Inc.
RR 1, Box 182
Brushton, New York 12916

PREFACE.

THE purpose of this little work is to present in the most concise and condensed form possible the various teachings upon the subjects of health, health reform, and allied matters, which are to be found in the writings of Mrs. E. G. White. The numerous paragraphs which have been brought together in this volume have been selected from many thousands of printed pages which have appeared in various forms from Mrs. White's pen, within the last thirty-four years, and in addition a large mass of manuscript which has never before appeared in print.

The compilers of the work have not attempted to make it exhaustive as regards subject matter, but rather to make it comprehensively representative of the principles of hygienic and sanitary reform which have been set forth in the writings referred to.

In the selection of paragraphs relating to each particular phase of the great question considered, an effort has been made to avoid unnecessary repetition, yet in a few instances, to render the thought more clear, the repetition of brief, pointed sentences has been allowed. The most conscientious care has been exercised in the making of extracts, to preserve the proper setting of the thought expressed. To do this without circumlocution has required, in a few instances, slight verbal changes in connecting words or phrases, but not in a single instance has the thought expressed been modified in the slightest degree.

It is believed that those whose knowledge of the writings from which these excerpts have been drawn has inspired confidence in them as a source of important truths, will appreciate this volume as a ready reference book in which can be easily found, by the aid of the table of contents and the index, a larger number of seed thoughts and clear expressions of fundamental principles upon the subjects treated than in any other volume of similar size which has ever appeared in print. To save space, abbreviations have been employed in the place of the titles of well-known works. These are explained on page 8.

PREFACE TO THE THIRD EDITION.

ALTHOUGH but a few months have elapsed since the first edition of this work was issued, a third edition is already demanded. The interest in the unique subject-matter presented is most gratifying to both compiler and publishers. Wherever it has been received, the work has been recognized as a veritable storehouse of seed thoughts relating to the great practical themes with which it deals. This edition contains two additional chapters, "God in Nature." and "The Spirit Filled Life," and also an appendix of parallel Scripture references, which will be found exceedingly helpful in making clear to the mind of the reader the fact that the principles presented in this work are not mere human inventions, but are a part of the divine order appointed for the human family at the beginning, and which is to be restored when all things shall be made new. It may be added that the compiler has carefully revised the entire work, making slight emendations and additions here and there in nearly every chapter, but, as before, without change in the original text from which the compilation has been made.

CONTENTS.

KEY TO ABBREVIATIONS.

C. E.— Christian Education.
C. T.— Christian Temperance.
F. of F.— Facts of Faith, found in Spiritual Gifts, Vol. 4.
G. W.— Gospel Workers.
H. R.— Health Reformer.
H. to L.— How to Live.
M. M.— Medical Missionary.
M. of B.— Mount of Blessing.
P. P.— Patriarchs and Proph-ets.
R. and H.— Review and Herald.
S. A.— Solemn Appeal.

S. of T.— Signs of the Times.
S. to C.— Steps to Christ.
Sp. Instr. on Ed. Work.— Spe-cial Instruction on Educa-tional Work.
S. T.— Special Testimony to Ministers and Workers.
S. T. on E.— Special Testi-mony on Education.
T.— Testimonies for the Church.
U. T.— Unpublished Testimo-nies.
Y. I.— Youth's Instructor.

HEALTHFUL LIVING.

CHAPTER I.

OUR BODIES, TEMPLES OF THE HOLY GHOST.

1. God is the owner of the whole man. Soul, body, and spirit are his. God gave his only begotten Son for the body as well as the soul, and our entire life belongs to God, to be consecrated to his service, that through the exercise of every faculty he has given, we may glorify him.—*Y. I., Sept. 7, 1893.*

God's Workmanship.

2. Jehovah has given a specimen of himself; for man was made in the image of God.—*U. T., Jan. 11, 1897.*

3. The living organism is God's property. It belongs to him by creation and by redemption; and by a misuse of any of our powers we rob God of the honor due him.— *U. T., Aug. 30, 1896.*

4. We are God's workmanship, and his word declares that we are "fearfully and wonderfully made." He has prepared this wonderful habitation for the mind; it is "curiously wrought," a temple which the Lord himself has fitted up for the indwelling of the Holy Spirit.— *S. T. on E., p. 33.*

5. The very flesh in which the soul tabernacles, and through which it works, is the Lord's.— *U. T., Oct. 12, 1896.*

Creation's Crown.

6. Man was the crowning act of the creation of God, made in the image of God, and designed to be a counterpart of God. . . . Man is very dear to God, because he was formed in his own image. This fact should impress us with the importance of teaching by precept and example the sin of defiling, by the indulgence of appetite or by any other sinful practise, the body which is designed to represent God to the world.— *R. and H., 1895, No. 25.*

7. The wonderful mechanism of the human body does not receive half the care that is often given to a mere lifeless machine.— *G. W., p. 175.*

Personal Rights.

8. Have I not the right to do as I please with my own body? — No, you have no moral right, because you are violating the laws of life and health which God has given you.   You are the Lord's property,— his by creation and his by redemption. Every human being is under obligation to preserve the living machinery that is so fearfully and wonderfully made. —*U. T., May 19, 1897.*

9. The physical organism should have special care, that the powers of the body may not be dwarfed, but developed to their full extent.— *Y. I., July 27, 1893.*

10. The health should be as sacredly guarded as the character.—*C. T., p. 83.*

11. Jesus did not ignore the claims of the body. He had respect for the physical condition of man, and went about healing the sick, and restoring their

faculties to those suffering from their loss.   How in-
cumbent, then, is it upon us to preserve the natural
health with which God has endowed us, and to avoid
dwarfing or weakening our powers.—*H. R.*

12. As they more fully understand the human
body, the wonderful work of God's hand, formed in
the image of the divine, they will seek to bring their
bodies into subjection to the noble powers of the
mind.   The body will be regarded by them as a
wonderful structure, formed by the Infinite Designer,
and given into their charge to be kept in harmonious
action.— *H. R.* **Mind Su-
preme.**

13. The obligation we owe to God in presenting
to him clean, pure, healthy bodies is not comprehended.— *U. T., May 19, 1897.*

14. Christ is to live in his human agents, and
work through their faculties, and act through their
capabilities.— *M. of B., p. 128.* **Christ In
Man.**

15. When human agents choose the will of God,
and are conformed to the character of Christ, Jesus
acts through their organs and faculties.— *S. T.,
No. 3, p. 49.*

16. The Spirit of Christ is to take possession of
the organs of speech, of the mental powers, of the
physical and moral powers.— *S. T., No. 6, p. 53.*

17. Our very bodies are not our own, to treat as
we please, to cripple by habits that lead to decay,
making it impossible to render to God perfect service.   Our lives and all our faculties belong to him.
He is caring for us every moment ; he keeps the living machinery in action; if we were left to run it for **Service**

one moment, we should die. We are absolutely dependent upon God.— *U. T., Oct. 12, 1896.*

18. It was a wonderful thing for God to create man, to make mind. He created him that every faculty might be the faculty of the divine mind. The glory of God is to be revealed in the creating of man in God's image, and in his redemption. One soul is of more value than a world. The Lord Jesus is the author of our being, and he is also the author of our redemption; and every one who will enter the kingdom of God must develop a character that is the counterpart of the character of God. None can dwell with God in a holy heaven but those who bear his likeness. Those who are redeemed will be over-comers; they will be elevated, pure, one with Christ. — *S. T., May 31, 1896.*

CHAPTER II.

DUTY TO STUDY THE LAWS OF LIFE.

19. It is our duty to study the laws that govern our being, and conform to them. Ignorance in these things is sin.— *U. T.*, *Aug. 25, 1897.*

20. From the first dawn of reason, the human mind should become intelligent in regard to the physical structure. We may behold and admire the work of God in the natural world, but the human habitation is the most wonderful.— *U. T.*, *Jan. 11, 1897.*

21. A practical knowledge of the science of human life is necessary in order to glorify God in our bodies. It is therefore of the highest importance that among studies selected for childhood, physiology should occupy the first place.— *H. R.*

Physiology as a Study.

22. It is well that physiology is introduced into the common schools as a branch of education. All children should study it. It should be regarded as the basis of all educational effort. And then parents should see to it that practical hygiene be added. This will make their knowledge of physiology of practical benefit.— *H. R.*

23. We have special duties resting upon us. We should be acquainted with our physical structure and the laws controlling natural life. While Greek and Latin, which are seldom of any advantage, are made

a study by many, physiology and hygiene are barely touched upon. The study to which to give thought is that which concerns natural life, a knowledge of oneself. . . . It is the house in which we live that we need to preserve, that we may do honor to God who has redeemed us. We need to know how to preserve the living machinery, that our soul, body, and spirit may be consecrated to his service. As rational beings we are deplorably ignorant of the body and its requirements. While the schools we have established have taken up the study of physiology, they have not taken hold with the decided energy they should. They have not practised intelligently that which they have received in knowledge, and do not realize that unless it is practised, the body will decay. . . . This living machinery should be understood. Every part of its wonderful mechanism should be carefully studied.— *U. T.*, *May 19, 1897.*

Ignorance of Physical Laws.

24. Physical life cannot be treated in a haphazard manner. Awaken to your responsibilities.— *U. T.*, *Aug. 25, 1897.*

25. Ignorance of physiology and neglect to observe the laws of health have brought many to the grave who might have lived to labor and study intelligently.— *S. T.*, *Feb.*, *1894, p. 13.*

26. To become acquainted with the wonderful human organism,— the bones, muscles, stomach, liver, bowels, heart, and pores of the skin,— and to understand the dependence of one organ upon another for the healthful action of all, is a study in

which most mothers take no interest.— *T., V. III, p. 136.*

27. Study that marvelous organism, the human system, and the laws by which it is governed.— *C. T., p. 120.*

28. If people would reason from cause to effect, and would follow the light which shines upon them, they would pursue a course which would insure health, and the mortality would be far less. . . . All who possess common capabilities should understand the wants of their own system.— *H. to L., Chap. 3, p. 51.*

How to Reduce Mortality.

29. It is of the highest importance that men and women be instructed in the science of human life, and in the best means of preserving and acquiring physical health. Especially is youth the time to lay up a stock of knowledge to be put in daily practise through life.— *H. R.*

Learn in Youth.

30. Those who have occupied positions of influence have not appreciated the work which has been so long neglected. . . . They consider it far more important to become learners upon subjects of less consequence to the human agent. Thousands upon thousands know nothing of the body, and how to care for it. David declared, "I am fearfully and wonderfully made." And when God has given us such a habitation, why should not every apartment be critically examined?— *U. T., Jan. 11, 1897.*

31. It is best for those who claim to be sons and daughters of God to avail themselves, while they can, of the opportunities now presented to gain a knowledge of the human system, and how it may be pre-

served in health. . . . The Lord will not work a
miracle to preserve any one in health who will not
make an effort to obtain knowledge within his reach
concerning this wonderful habitation that God has
given. By the study of the human organism we are
to learn to correct what may be wrong in our habits,
and which, if left uncorrected, will bring the sure
result, disease and suffering, that make life a burden.
. . . Let the mind become intelligent, and the will
be placed on the Lord's side, and there will be a
wonderful improvement in the physical health. But
this can never be accomplished in mere human
strength.—*M. M., V. II, p. 216.*

**Duty of
Ministers.**   32. The ministers in our land need to become
acquainted with the science of physiology. Then
they will be intelligent in regard to the laws that
govern physical life, and their bearings upon the
health of mind and soul. Then they will be able to
speak correctly upon this subject. In their obedience to physical laws they are to hold forth the word
of life to the people, and lead up higher and still
higher in the work of reform.— *U. T., Jan. 11, 1897.*

33. In order to be fitted for translation, the people
of God must know themselves. They must understand in regard to their own physical frames, that
they may be able with the psalmist to exclaim, "I
will praise thee, for I am fearfully and wonderfully
made." — *T., V. I, p. 486.*

CHAPTER III.

THE GREAT DECALOGUE.

34. He who hungers and thirsts after God will seek for an understanding of the laws which the God of wisdom has impressed upon creation. These laws are a transcript of his character. They must control all who enter the heavenly and better country. — *U. T., Aug. 30, 1896.* **Character of God.**

35. God's law is written by his own finger upon every nerve, every muscle, every faculty which has been entrusted to man.— *U. T., Aug. 30, 1896.*

36. God in his wisdom has established natural laws for the proper control of our dress, our appetites, and our passions, and he requires of us obedience in every particular.— *R. and H., 1883, No. 41.* **Obedience to Law.**

37. The transgression of physical law is transgression of God's law. Our Creator is Jesus Christ. He is the author of our being. He is the author of the physical law as he is the author of the moral law. And the human being who is careless and reckless of the habits and practises that concern his physical life and health, sins against God. God is not reverenced, respected, or recognized. This is shown by the injury done to the body in violation of physical law.— *U. T., May 19, 1897.* **Physical Sin.**

38. God loves his creatures with a love that is both tender and strong. He has established the laws

2

of nature ; but his laws are not arbitrary exactions. Every "Thou shalt not," whether in physical or moral law, contains or implies a promise. If it is obeyed, blessings will attend our steps; if it is disobeyed, the result is danger and unhappiness. — *T., No. 32, p. 201.*

Blessings Follow Obedience.

39. Health, strength, and- happiness depend upon immutable laws ; but these laws cannot be obeyed where there is no anxiety to become acquainted with them. — *H. R.*

40. A knowledge of the laws by which health is secured and preserved is of pre-eminent importance. — *S. of T., 1886, No. 33.*

41. Indifference and ignorance in regard to the laws which govern our being are sins so common that we have learned to look upon them with undue tolerance. — *H. R.*

42. We have no right wantonly to violate a single principle of the laws of health. — *R. and H., 1884, No. 31.*

43. God is greatly dishonored by the way in which man treats his organism, and he will not work a miracle to counteract a perverse violation of the laws of life and health. — *U. T., Aug. 30, 1896.*

44. The Lord has made it a part of his plan that man's reaping shall be according to his sowing. — *U. T., May 19, 1897.*

Heredity

45. Wherever the habits of the parents are contrary to physical law, the injury done to themselves will be repeated in future generations. — *U. T., Jan. 11, 1897.*

46. You should move out from principle, in harmony with natural law, irrespective of feeling.— *T., V. III, p. 76.*

47. To make plain natural law, and urge the obedience of it, is the work that accompanies the third angel's message to prepare a people for the coming of the Lord.— *T., V. III, p. 161.*

48. A flower of the field must have its root in the soil; it must have air, dew, showers, and sunshine. It will flourish only as it receives these advantages, and all are from God. So with man.— *Special Testimony to R. and H. Office, Sept. 19, 1895, p. 36.*

49. God calls for reformers to stand in defense of the laws he has established to govern the human system, and to maintain an elevated standard in the training of the mind and culture of the heart.— *S. T., No. 3, p. 22.*

50. It is the duty of every human being, for his own sake and for the sake of humanity, to inform himself or herself in regard to the laws of organic life, and conscientiously to obey them. . . . It is the duty of every person to become intelligent in regard to disease and its causes. You must study your Bible, in order to understand the value that the Lord places on the men whom Christ has purchased at such an infinite price. Then we should become acquainted with the laws of life, that every action of the human agent may be in perfect harmony with the laws of God. When there is so great peril in ignorance, is it not best to be wise in regard to the human habitation fitted up by our Creator, and over which he desires that we shall be faithful stewards? — *U. T., Dec. 4, 1896.*

Knowledge a Duty.

CHAPTER IV.

NATURAL LAW PART OF THE LAW OF GOD.

51. The same law obtains in the spiritual as in the natural world.—*M. of B., p. 126.*

52. The transgression of the physical law is transgression of God's law. Our Creator is Jesus Christ. —*U. T., May 19, 1897.*

Natural Law Divine. 53. Every law governing the human machinery is to be considered just as truly divine in origin, in character, and in importance as the word of God. Every careless action, any abuse put upon the wonderful mechanism, by disregarding his specified laws of the human habitation, is a violation of God's law. This law embraces the treatment of the entire being. *U. T., Jan. 11, 1897.*

54. God's law is written by his own finger upon every nerve, every muscle, every faculty which has been entrusted to man.—*U. T., Aug. 30, 1896.*

55. God has formed laws to govern every part of our constitutions, and these laws which he has placed in our being are divine, and for every transgression **Its Penalty.** there is a fixed penalty, which sooner or later must be realized.—*H. R.*

56. Our first duty, one which we owe to God, to ourselves, and to our fellow men, is to obey the laws of God, which include the laws of health.— *T., V. III, p. 164.*

57. The laws governing the physical nature are as truly divine in their origin and character as the law of the ten commandments. Man is fearfully and wonderfully made; for Jehovah has inscribed his law by his own mighty hand on every part of the human body.— *U. T., Aug. 5, 1896.*

58. It is just as much sin to violate the laws of our being as to break one of the ten commandments, for we cannot do either without breaking God's law. — *T., V. II, p. 70.*

Physical Sin.

59. The human being who is careless and reckless of the habits and practises that concern his physical life and health, sins against God.— *U. T., May 19, 1897.*

60. A violation of these laws is a violation of the immutable law of God, and the penalty will surely follow.—*R. and H., 1883, No. 41.*

CHAPTER V.

BLESSINGS FROM OBEYING NATURAL LAW.

61. Those who understand something of the wisdom and beneficence of his laws, and perceive the evidences of God's love and the blessings that result from obedience, will come to regard their duties and obligations from an altogether different point of view. Instead of looking upon the observance of the laws of health as a matter of sacrifice and self-denial, they will regard it, as it really is, an inestimable blessing. — *C. T., p. 120.*

62. All our enjoyment or suffering may be traced to obedience or transgression of natural law.— *T., V. III, p. 161.*

Co-operation. 63. God, the Creator of our bodies, has arranged every fiber and nerve and sinew and muscle, and has pledged himself to keep the machinery in order if the human agent will co-operate with him and refuse to work contrary to the laws which govern the human system.— *U. T., Aug. 30, 1896.*

64. A careful conformity to the laws which God has implanted in our being will insure health, and there will not be a breaking down of the constitution. — *H. R.*

65. God has pledged himself to keep this machinery in healthful action if the human agent will obey his laws, and co-operate with him.— *U. T., Jan. 11, 1897.*

66. Every "Thou shall not," whether in physical or moral law, contains or implies a promise. If it is obeyed, blessings will attend our steps.— *T., No. 32, p. 201.*

67. He requires us to obey natural law, to preserve physical health.— *T., V. III, p. 63.*

68. If Christians will keep the body in subjection, and bring all their appetites and passions under the control of enlightened conscience, feeling it a duty that they owe to God and to their neighbors to obey the laws which govern health and life, they will have the blessing of physical and mental vigor. They will have moral power to engage in the warfare against Satan; and in the name of him who conquered appetite in their behalf, they may be more than conquerors on their own account.— *T., V. IV, p. 36.*

69. If laborers who are now in the field had intelligently used their physical and mental powers according to the laws of hygiene, they would not only have been able to become proficient in common branches of education, but would have been versed in different languages, and thus would have been qualified to become missionaries in foreign countries. — *Y. I., May 31, 1894.*

Adherence to Principle.

70. The souls and bodies of people have been fast becoming a corrupted mass of disease. This would not have been the case if those who claimed to believe the truth had lived out its sacred principles in their lives.—*U. T., Jan. 11, 1897.*

71. If man had obeyed the laws of Jehovah in his natural laws, the image of God would have been revealed in him.— *Ibid.*

CHAPTER VI.

THE CONSEQUENCE OF VIOLATING NATURAL LAW

72. Proportionately as nature's laws are transgressed, mind and soul become enfeebled. . . . Physical suffering of every type is seen. . . . Suffering must follow this course of action. The vital force of the system cannot bear up under the tax placed upon it, and it finally breaks down.— *U. T., Aug. 30, 1896.*

Cause of Sickness.

73. Every misuse of any part of our organism is a violation of the law which God designs shall govern us in these matters ; and by violating this law, human beings corrupt themselves. Sickness, disease of every kind, ruined constitutions, premature decay, untimely deaths,— these are a result of a violation of nature's laws.— *U. T., Aug. 30, 1896.*

74. Sickness is caused by violating the laws of health; it is the result of violating nature's laws.— *T., V. III, p. 164.*

75. The gloom and despondency supposed to be the result of obedience to God's moral law are often attributable to disregard of physical laws.— *S. of T., 1885, No. 42.*

Diseased Souls.

76. Everything that conflicts with natural law creates a diseased condition of the soul.— *R. and H., 1881, No. 4.*

[24]

77. The moral powers are weakened because men and women will not live in obedience to the laws of health, and make this great subject a personal duty. — *T., V. III, p. 140.*

78. The Lord has made it a part of his plan that **We Reap What We Sow.** man's reaping shall be according to his sowing. And this is the explanation of the misery and suffering in our world, which is charged back upon God. The man who serves himself, and makes a god of his stomach, will reap that which is the sure result of the violation of nature's laws. He who abuses any organ of the body to gratify lustful appetites and debased passions will bear testimony to the same in his countenance. He has sown to fleshly lusts, and he will just as surely realize the consequence. He is like a hunted being; he is a slave to passion, the chains of which he is unwilling to break. And at last he is left of God, without conviction, without mercy, without hope, to destroy himself. He is left to the natural processes of corrupting practises which degrade him beneath the brute creation. His sinfulness has ruined the mechanism of the living machinery, and nature's laws, transgressed, become his tormentors.— *U. T., May 19, 1897.*

79. Satan knows that he cannot overcome man **Control of Will.** unless he can control his will. He can do this by deceiving men so they will co-operate with him in transgressing the laws of nature, which is transgression of the law of God.— *U. T., Jan. 11, 1897.*

80. The results which Satan has, through his specious temptations, brought about, he uses to taunt God **Satan Taunting God.** with. He presents before God the appearance of

the human being whom Christ has purchased as his property. And what an unsightly representation of his Maker! God is dishonored, because man has corrupted his ways before the Lord.— *U. T., Jan. 11, 1897.*

81. One human being becomes Satan's copartner to tempt, allure, and deceive his fellow men to vicious practises; and the sure result is diseased bodies, because of the violation of moral law. "Because iniquity shall abound, the love of many shall wax cold." It is Satan's determined purpose to deceive the human family so that he can bring them as a mass on his side, to work with him in making void the law of God. Thus he finds agencies which multiply his efficiency. And as they do this, he rules them with a rod of iron. And not only the human race, but the brute creation also are made to suffer through Satan's attributes wrought out through the human agent.— *U. T., Jan. 11, 1897.*

CHAPTER VII.

NATURAL LAW; HOW VIOLATED.

82. Needlessly to transgress the laws of our being **General Statements.** is a violation of the law of God.— *T., V. II, p. 538.*

83. If we unnecessarily injure our constitutions, we dishonor God, for we transgress the laws of our being.— *H. R.*

84. If appetite, which should be strictly guarded and controlled, is indulged to the injury of the body, the penalty of transgression will surely result.— *U. T., Aug. 30, 1896.*

85. Every careless action, any abuse put upon the Lord's mechanism, by disregarding his specified laws in the human habitation, is a violation of God's law. — *U. T., Jan. 11, 1897.*

86. Intemperance of any kind is a violation of the laws of our being.— *H. R.*

87. The laws of our being cannot be more success- **Indulgence** fully violated than by crowding upon the stomach **of Appetite.** unhealthful food just because it is craved by a morbid appetite.— *H. to L., Chap. 1, p. 52.*

88. Eating merely to please the appetite is a transgression of nature's laws.— *U. T., Aug. 30, 1896.*

89. Any course of action in eating, drinking, or dressing that is unhealthful injures the fine works of the human machinery, and interferes with God's order. Obstructions are created in bone, brain,

and muscle, which destroy this wonderful machinery that God has organized to be kept in order. Any misuse of the delicate workmanship results in suffering.— *U. T.*, *May 19, 1897.*

90. God has not changed, neither does he propose to change, our physical organism, in order that we may violate a single law without feeling the effects of its violation. . . . By indulging their inclinations and appetites, men violate the laws of life and health ; and if they obey conscience, they must be controlled by principle in their eating and dressing, rather than be led by inclination, fashion, and appetite.— *H. R.*

Lack of Exercise. 91. Neglecting to exercise the entire body, or a portion of it, will bring on morbid conditions. Inaction of any of the organs of the body will be followed by a decrease in size and strength of the muscles, and will cause the blood to flow sluggishly through the blood-vessels.— *T., V. III, p. 76.*

CHAPTER VIII.

HEALTH.

92. Health is a great treasure. It is the richest General Statements. possession that mortal can have. Wealth, honor, or learning is dearly purchased, if it be at the loss of the vigor of health. None of these attainments can secure happiness if health is wanting.— *C. E., p. 16.*

93. The health should be as sacredly guarded as the character.— *C. T., p. 83.*

94. Our physical, mental, and moral powers are not our own, but lent us of God to be used in his service.— *H. R.*

95. The more perfect our health, the more perfect will be our labor.— *T., V. III, p. 13.*

96. The importance of the health of the body is to be taught as a Bible requirement.— *U. T., Aug. 30, 1896.*

97. All who profess to be followers of Jesus should feel that a duty rests upon them to preserve their bodies in the best condition of health, that their minds may be clear to comprehend heavenly things. — *T., V. II, p. 522.*

98. That time is well spent which is directed to the establishment and preservation of sound physical and mental health. . . . It is easy to lose health, but it is difficult to regain it.— *R. and H., 1884, No. 39.*

[29]

Circulation.   99. Perfect health depends upon perfect circulation.— *T., V. II, p. 531.*

100. The health of the entire system depends upon the healthy action of the respiratory organs.— *H. to L., Chap. 6, p. 57.*

101. If we would have health, we must live for it. — *H. R.*

102. We can ill afford to dwarf or cripple a single function of mind or body by overwork, or by abuse of any part of the living machinery.— *R. and H., 1884, No. 39.*

103. A sound body is required for a sound intellect.— *C. E., p. 17.*

Faith and Practise.   104. When we do all we can on our part to have health, then may we expect that the blessed results will follow, and we can ask God in faith to bless our efforts for the preservation of health. He will then answer our prayer, if his name can be glorified thereby; but let all understand that they have a work to do. God will not work in a miraculous manner to preserve the health of persons who are taking a sure course to make themselves sick.— *H. to L., Chap. 4, p. 64.*

105. A careful conformity to the laws God has implanted in our being will insure health, and there will not be a breaking down of the constitution.— *H. R.*

How to Preserve Health.   106. Many have inquired of me, What course shall I take best to preserve my health? My answer is, Cease to transgress the laws of your being; cease to gratify a depraved appetite, eat simple food, dress healthfully, which will require modest simplicity,

work healthfully, and you will not be sick. . . .
Many are suffering in consequence of the transgression of their parents. They cannot be censured for
their parents' sins, but it is nevertheless their duty
to ascertain wherein their parents violated the laws
of their being; and wherein their parents' habits
were wrong, they should change their own course,
and place themselves, by correct habits, in a better
relation to health.— *H. R.*

107. The harmonious, healthy action of all the
powers of body and mind results in happiness ; the
more elevated and refined the powers, the more
pure and unalloyed the happiness. An aimless life
is a living death. The mind should dwell upon
themes relating to our eternal interests. This will
be conducive to health of body and mind.— *R. and
H., 1884, No. 31.*

108. God has pledged himself to keep this living
machinery in healthful action if the human agent
will obey his laws and co-operate with God.— *U. T.,
Jan. 11, 1897.*

CHAPTER IX.

HEALTH REFORM.

109. The Lord has given his people a message in regard to health reform. This light has been shining upon their pathway for thirty years. . . . Can he be pleased, when half the workers laboring in a place teach that the principles of health reform are as closely allied to the third angel's message as the arm is to the body, to have their co-workers, by their practise, teach principles that are entirely opposite? Testimony after testimony has been given which should have brought about great reforms. . . . The **Light Given.** light which God has given upon health reform cannot be trifled with without injury to those who attempt it ; and no man can hope to succeed in the work of God while, by precept and example, he acts in opposition to the light which God has sent.—*Special Testimony for Ministers and Workers, No. 7, p. 40.*

110. The Lord has inspired me to write the very things that are essential for this time in regard to the special attention we must give to the care of the body.— *U. T., May 19, 1897.*

111. We begin to comprehend better the light given years ago,—that health reform principles would be as an entering wedge to be followed by a religious influence.— *U. T., Nov. 19, 1895.*

112. Your interest and effort are to be given, not to the health question alone, but to making known the truths for these last times, truths that are deciding the destiny of souls.— *U. T., May 29, 1896.*

113. There is real common sense in health reform. — *C. T., p. 57.*

Common Sense in Health Reform.

114. The principles of health reform have the highest authority, and deserve a wider sphere than has yet been given them by many who profess present truth.— *U. T., Nov. 8, 1896.*

115. The Lord does not give light on health reform that it may be disregarded by those who are in positions of influence and authority. The Lord means just what he says, and he is to be honored in what he says.— *U. T., Nov. 8, 1896.*

116. There are those who have stood directly in the way of the advance of health reform. They have held the people back by their indifferent or depreciatory remarks, and their supposed pleasantries and jokes. . . . Had all walked unitedly in the light, from the time it was first given on the subject, there would have been an army of sensible arguments employed to vindicate the work of God. But it has only been by the most aggressive movements that any advance has been made. . . .

The ministers of our land should become intelligent upon health reform. They need to become acquainted with the science of physiology. Then they will be intelligent in regard to the laws that govern physical life and their bearings upon the health of mind and soul, and will be able to speak correctly upon this subject. In their obedience to

Duty of Ministers.

physical laws they are to hold forth the word of life
to the people, and lead up higher and still higher in
the work of reform.— *U. T., Jan. 11, 1897.*

117. Blindness mingles with the want of moral
courage to deny your appetite, to lift the cross,
which means to take up the very duties that cut
across the natural appetites and passions.— *U. T.,
Nov. 5, 1896.*

118. Many have misinterpreted health reform,
and have received perverted ideas of what consti-
tutes right living.— *Y. I., May 31, 1894.*

119. Nature's path is the road God marks out,
and it is broad enough for any Christian.— *T., V.
III, p. 63.*

**Avoid
Extremes.**   120. Health reformers, above all others, should
be careful to shun extremes.— *T., V. II, p. 538.*

121. All are bound by the most sacred obligations
to God to heed the sound philosophy and genuine
experience which he is now giving them in reference
to health reform.   He designs that the great subject
of health reform shall be agitated, and the public
mind deeply stirred to investigate.— *T., V. III,
p. 162.*

122. Do not catch hold of isolated ideas, and
make them a test, criticising others whose practise
may not agree with your opinion; but study the
subject broadly and deeply.— *C. T., pp. 119, 120.*

123. The lack of stability in regard to the principles of health reform is a true index of their character and their spiritual strength.— *T., V. II, p. 481.*

124. When we adopt the health reform, we should

adopt it from a sense of duty, not because somebody else has adopted it.— *T.*, *V. II, p. 371.*

125. In reforms we would better come one step short of the mark than go one step beyond it. And if there is error at all, let it be on the side next to the people. . . . We must go no faster than we can take those with us whose consciences and intellects are convinced of the truths we advocate. We must meet the people where they are. . . . But we should be very cautious not to advance too fast, lest we be obliged to retrace our steps. . . . If we come to persons who have not been enlightened in regard to health reform, and present our strongest positions at first, there is danger of their becoming discouraged as they see how much they have to give up, so that they will make no effort to reform. We must lead the people along patiently and gradually, remembering the hole of the pit from which we were digged.— *T.*, *V. III, pp. 20, 21.*

The Educational Process.

126. The greatest objection to health reform is that this people do not live it out.— *T.*, *V. II, p. 486.*

127. Guilt rests upon us who as a people have had much light, because we have not appreciated or improved the light given upon health reform. . . . This is not a matter to be trifled with, to be passed off with a jest.— *M. M.*, *V. II, p. 216.*

Relation of Health Reform to the Present Closing Work.

An Entering Wedge.

128. This work we begin to comprehend better,— the light given years ago,— that health reform principles would be as an entering wedge to be followed by a religious influence. To voice the words of John, "Behold the Lamb of God, which taketh away the sin of the world."— *U. T , Nov. 19, 1895.*

129. In the time of confusion and trouble such as never was since there was a nation, the uplifted Saviour will be presented to the people in all lands and in all places, that all who look may live.—*S. T., " Matters in B. C.," p. 7.*

130. The need of healthful habits is a part of the gospel which must be presented to the people by those who hold forth the word of life.— *U. T., Aug. 30, 1896.*

131. Take the living principles of health reform into communities that to a large degree are ignorant of what they should do.— *S. T., No. 5, p. 5.*

Preparation for Loud Cry.

132. The health reform, I was shown, is a part of the third angel's message, and is just as closely connected with it as the arm and hand with the body. I saw that we as a people must make an advance move in this great work. Ministers and people must act in concert. God's people are not prepared for the loud cry of the third angel; they have a work to do for themselves which they should not leave for God to do for them. It is an individual work; one cannot do it for another.— *T., V. I, p. 486.*

133. You have stumbled at the health reform. It appears to you to be a needless appendix to the truth. It is not so; it is a part of the truth.— *T., V. I, p. 546.*

134. Its place is among those subjects which set forth the preparatory work to meet the events brought to view by the message ; among them it is prominent.— *T., V. I, p. 559.*

135. The presentation of health principles must be united with this message, but must not be independent of it or in any way take the place of it.—*U. T., May 27, 1896.*

136. This branch of the Lord's work has not received due attention, and through this neglect much has been lost.— *C. T., p. 121.*

137. Much of the prejudice that prevents the truth of the third angel's message from reaching the hearts of the people, might be removed if more attention were given to health reform. When people become interested in this subject, the way is often prepared for the entrance of other truths.— *C. T., p. 121.*

Prejudice Removed.

138. Those who proclaim the message should teach health reform also. . . . Satan and his angels are seeking to hinder this work of reform, and will do all they can to perplex and burden those who heartily engage in it.— *C. T., p. 122.*

139. To make plain natural law, and urge the obedience of it, is the work that accompanies the third angel's message, to prepare a people for the coming of the Lord.— *T., V. III, p. 161.*

Object of Health Reform.

140. Let it ever be kept before the mind that the great object of hygienic reform is to secure the highest possible development of mind and soul and body. — *C. T., p. 120*

141. He who cherishes the light which God has given him upon health reform has an important aid in the work of becoming sanctified through the truth, and fitted for immortality.— *C. T., p. 10.*

142. God requires all who believe the truth to make special persevering efforts to place themselves in the best possible condition of bodily health, for a solemn and important work is before us. Health of body and mind is required for this work ; it is as essential to a healthy religious experience, to advancement in the Christian life, and progress in holiness, as is the hand or foot to the human body.— *T., V. I, p. 619.*

Relation of Health Reform to Spirituality.

Control of the Will.

143. Satan knows that he cannot overcome man unless he can control his will. He can do this by deceiving man so that he will co-operate with him in transgressing the laws of nature.— *U. T., Jan. 11, 1897.*

144. Anything that lessens the physical power enfeebles the mind and makes it less clear to discriminate between good and evil, between right and wrong.— *S. T., on E., p. 35.*

145. The principles of health reform, . . . which are adopted by him who gives the word of God to others, will have a molding influence upon

his work, and upon those with whom he labors. If his principles are wrong, he can and will misrepresent the truth to others ; if he accepts the truth which appeals to reason rather than to perverted appetite, his influence for the right will be decided.— *S. T., No. 7, p. 41.*

146. One reason why we do not enjoy more of the blessing of the Lord is, we do not heed the light which he has been pleased to give us in regard to the laws of life and health.— *R. and H., 1883, No. 19.*

Light Unheeded.

147. The lack of stability in regard to the principles of health reform is a true index of their character and their spiritual strength.— *T., V. II, p. 487.*

148. It is not possible for us to glorify God while living in violation of the laws of life.— *H. R.*

149. All who profess to be followers of Jesus should feel that a duty rests upon them to preserve their bodies in the best condition of health, that their minds may be clear to comprehend heavenly things.— *T., V. II, p. 522.*

150. If our physical habits are not right, our mental and moral powers cannot be strong ; for great sympathy exists between the physical and the moral. . . . Habits which lower the standard of physical health, enfeeble the mental and moral strength.— *T., V. III, pp. 50, 51.*

The Influence of Habit.

151. If you pursue a wrong course, and indulge in wrong habits of eating, and thereby weaken the intellectual powers, you will not place that high estimate upon salvation and eternal life which will inspire you to conform your life to the life of Christ; you will not make those earnest, self-sacrificing

efforts for entire conformity to the will of God which his word requires, and which are necessary to give you a moral fitness for the finishing touch of immortality.— *T., V. II, p. 66.*

152. In order to live a perfect life, we must live in harmony with those natural laws which govern our being.— *T., V. III, p. 163.*

Effects upon the Mind.

153. That which darkens the skin and makes it dingy, also clouds the spirits, and destroys the cheerfulness and peace of mind. . . . Every wrong habit which injures the health of the body, reacts in effect upon the mind.— *H. R.*

154. Those things which fret and derange the stomach will have a benumbing influence upon the finer feelings of the heart.— *T., V. II, p. 537.*

155. The gloom and despondency supposed to be the result of obedience to God's moral law is often attributable to disregard of physical law. Those whose moral faculties are beclouded by disease are not the ones rightly to represent the Christian life, and show forth the joys of salvation or the beauties of holiness. They are too often in the fire of fanaticism, or the waters of cold indifference or stolid gloom.— *S. of T., No. 42, 1885.*

156. Unless they practise true temperance, they will not, they cannot, be susceptible to the sanctifying influence of the truth.— *C. T., p. 117.*

157. Eating, drinking, and dressing all have a direct bearing upon our spiritual advancement.— *Y. I., May 31, 1894.*

158. By indulging in a wrong course of action in eating and drinking, thousands upon thousands are

ruining their health, and not only is their health ruined, but their morals are corrupted, because diseased blood flows through their veins.— *U. T.*, *Aug. 30, 1896.*   **Morals Corrupted.**

159. Overeating prevents the free flow of thought and words, and that intensity of feeling which is so necessary in order to impress the truth upon the heart of the hearer.— *T., V. III, p. 310.*

160. Excessive eating of even the best of food will produce a morbid condition of the moral feelings. . . . Wrong habits of eating and drinking lead to errors in thought and action. Indulgence of appetite strengthens the animal propensities, giving them the ascendency over the mental and spiritual powers. . . . Everything that conflicts with natural law creates a diseased condition of the soul.— *R. and H.*, *1881, No. 4.*

161. Irregularity in eating and drinking, and improper dressing, deprave the mind and corrupt the heart, and bring the noble attributes of the soul in slavery to the animal passions.— *H. R.*

162. If those who profess to be Christians desire to solve the questions so perplexing to them,— why their minds are so dull, why their religious aspirations are so feeble,— they need not, in many instances, go farther than the table; here is cause enough, if there were no other.— *C. T., p. 83.*

163. A religious life can be more successfully gained and maintained if flesh meats are discarded; for a meat diet stimulates into intense activity lustful propensities, and enfeebles the spiritual and moral nature.— *U. T., Nov. 5, 1896.*

164. Children reared in a healthful way are much more easily controlled than those who are indulged in eating everything their appetite craves, and at all times. They are usually cheerful, contented, and healthy. Even the most stubborn, passionate, and wayward have become submissive, patient, and possessed of self-control by persistently following up this order of diet, united with a firm but kind management in regard to other matters.— *H. R.*

A Living Sacrifice.

165. The Lord requires a *living* sacrifice of mind, soul, body, and strength. All that we have and are is to be given to him, that we may answer the purpose of our creation.— *U. T., Aug. 25, 1897.*

166. True sanctification is not merely a theory, an emotion, or a form of words, but a living, active principle, entering into the every-day life. It requires that our habits of eating, drinking, and dressing be such as to secure the preservation of physical, mental, and moral health, that we may present to the Lord our bodies, not an offering corrupted by wrong habits, but a "living sacrifice, holy, acceptable unto God."— *R. and H., 1881, No. 4.*

167. It should ever be kept prominent that the great object to be attained through this channel is not only health, but perfection and the spirit of holiness, which cannot be attained with diseased bodies and minds. This object cannot be secured by working merely from the worldling's standpoint.— *T., V. I, p. 554.*

168. A diseased body causes a disordered brain, and hinders the work of sanctifying grace upon the mind and heart.— *H. R.*

169. If man will cherish the light that God in mercy gives him upon health reform, he may be sanctified through the truth, and fitted for immortality.— *T., V. III, p. 162.*

170. If Christians . . . obey the laws which govern health and life, they will have the blessing of physical and mental vigor. They will have moral power to engage in the warfare against Satan; and in the name of him who conquered appetite in their behalf, they may be more than conquerors on their own account.— *T., V. IV, pp. 35, 36.*

171. The character and efficiency of the work depend largely on the physical condition of the workers. . . . Many a sermon has received a dark shadow from the minister's indigestion. Health is an inestimable blessing, and one which is more closely allied to conscience and religion than many realize.— *G. W., p. 175.*

172. In order to render to God perfect service, we must have a clear conception of his will. This will require us to use only healthful food, prepared in a simple manner, that the fine nerves of the brain be not injured, making it impossible for us to discern the value of the atonement, and the priceless worth of the cleansing blood of Christ.— *R. and H., 1880, No. 12.*

173. God's way is to give man something that he **God's Plan.** has not, to make him something that he is not. Man's way is to get an easy place, and indulge appetite and selfish ambition. God's plan is to set man at work in reformatory lines, then he will learn by experience how long he has tampered with fleshly appetites, and

ministered to his own temperament, bringing weakness upon himself. God's way is to work in power. He gives grace if the sick man realizes that he needs it. God proposes to purify and refine the defiled soul, then he will implant in the heart his own righteousness and peace and health, and man will become **The Kingdom** complete in him. This is the kingdom of God within **Within.** you. Day by day men are revealing whether the kingdom of God is within them. If Christ rules in their hearts, they are gaining strength of principle, with power and ability to stand as faithful sentinels, true reformers. Then, like Daniel, they make impressions upon other hearts that will never be effaced, and their influence will be carried to all parts of the world.— *U. T., Oct. 12, 1896.*

Our Duty 174. It is the duty of those who have received **to Others.** light upon this important subject to manifest a greater interest for those who are still suffering for want of knowledge. Those who are looking for the soon appearing of their Saviour should be the last to manifest a lack of interest in this great work of reform. . . . This (2 Cor. 7 : 1) is our work as Christians, to cleanse our robes of character from every spot. The spirit must be in harmony with the Spirit of Christ; the habits must be in conformity to his will, in obedience to his requirements.— *R. and H., 1884, No. 31.*

CHAPTER X.

VITAL VIGOR AND ENERGY.

175. God has provided us with constitutional **General Statements.** force, which will be needed at different periods of our life.   If we recklessly exhaust this force by continual overtaxation, we shall sometime be losers. Our usefulness will be lessened, if not life itself destroyed.— *C. T., p. 65.*

176. God endowed man with so great vital force that he has withstood the accumulation of disease upon the race in consequence of perverted habits, and has continued for six thousand years. . . .

If Adam, at his creation, had not been endowed with twenty times as much vital force as men now have, the race, with their present habits of living in violation of natural law, would have become extinct.— *T., V. III, pp. 138, 139.*

177. The tree of life possessed the power to perpetuate life, and as long as they [Adam and Eve] ate of it, they could not die.   The lives of the antediluvians were protracted because of the life-giving power of this tree, which was transmitted to them from Adam and Eve.—*R. and H., 1897, No. 4.*

Conditions Conducive to Health and Vigor.

178. The Bible is a leaf from the tree of life, and **The Bible.** by eating it, by receiving it into our minds, we

shall grow strong to do the will of God.— *R. and H.*, *1897, No. 18.*

Exercise.   179. Neither are they willing to wait the slow process of nature to build up the overtaxed energies of the system.— *H. to L., Chap. 3, p. 60.*

186. Useful employment would bring into exercise the enfeebled muscles, enliven the stagnant blood, and the entire system would be invigorated to overcome bad conditions.— *H. R.*

181. If physical exercise were combined with mental exertion, the blood would be quickened in its circulation, the action of the heart would be more perfect, impure matter would be thrown off, and new life and vigor would be experienced in every part of the body.— *T., V. III, p. 490.*

182. If invalids would recover health, they should not discontinue physical exercise. . . . There will be increased vitality, which is so necessary to health.— *T., V. II, p. 529.*

Pure Air.   183. They are deprived in a great measure of air, which will invigorate them and give them energy and vitality. — *T., V. II, p. 533.*

184. Fresh air is the free blessing of Heaven, calculated to electrify the whole system.— *T., V. I, p. 701.*

Sleep.   185. Nature will restore their vigor and strength in their sleeping hours, if her laws are not violated. — *S. A., p. 62.*

Bathing.   186. Bathing helps the bowels, stomach, and liver, giving energy and new life to each.— *T., V. III, p. 70.*

187. The latter class do not exercise the mind; Influence of the Mind. their muscles are exercised while their brains are robbed of intellectual strength; just as the minds of thinking men are worked while their bodies are robbed of strength and vigor by their neglect to exercise the muscles. Those who are content to devote their lives to physical labor, and leave others to do the thinking for them, while they simply carry out what other brains have planned, will have strength of muscle, but feeble intellects. This class fall more readily if attacked by disease, because the system is vitalized by the electrical force of the brain to resist disease.— *T., V. III, p. 157.*

188. Bring to your aid the power of the will, which will resist cold, and will give energy to the nervous system.— *T., V. II, p. 533.*

Conditions Unfavorable to Strength and Vigor.

189. Misuse of the body shortens that period of Irregular Habits. time which God designs shall be used in his service. By allowing ourselves to form wrong habits, by keeping late hours, by gratifying appetite at the expense of health, we lay the foundation for feebleness. By neglecting to take physical exercise, by overworking mind or body, we unbalance the nervous system. Those who thus shorten their lives by disregarding nature's laws, are guilty of robbery before God.— *R. and H., 1896, No. 48.*

190. Those who make great exertions to accom- Overwork. plish just so much work in a given time, and continue to labor when their judgment tells them they should rest, are never gainers. They are living on borrowed

capital. They are expending the vital force which they will need at a future time. And when the energy they have so recklessly used, is demanded, they fail for want of it. If all the hours of the day are well improved, the work extended into the evening is so much extra, and the overtaxed system will suffer from the burden imposed upon it. I have been shown that those who do this often lose much more than they gain, for their energies are exhausted, and they labor on nervous excitement. They may not realize any immediate injury, but they are surely undermining their constitution.— *C. T., p. 65.*

Impure Air. 191. The effects produced by living in close, ill-ventilated rooms are these: The system becomes weakened, the circulation is depressed, the blood moves sluggishly through the system, because it is not purified and vitalized by the pure, invigorating air of heaven. The mind becomes depressed and gloomy, while the whole system is enervated.— *T., V. I, pp. 702, 703.*

A Disturbed Mind. 192. Doubt, perplexity, and excessive grief often sap the vital forces and induce nervous diseases of a most debilitating and distressing character.— *R. and H., 1883, No. 41.*

Errors in Diet. 193. Unhealthful habits of eating are injuring thousands and tens of thousands. Food should be thoroughly cooked, neatly prepared, and appetizing. — *U. T., Nov. 5, 1896.*

Cold Food. 194. I do not approve of eating much cold food, for the reason that the vitality must be drawn from the system to warm the food until it becomes of the same temperature as the stomach, before the work of digestion can be carried on.— *T.*, *V. II, p. 603*.

195. They eat improperly, and this calls their nervous energies to the stomach, and they have no vitality to expend in other directions.— *T.*, *V. II, p. 365*.

196. Children are permitted to indulge their tastes **Children.** freely, to eat at all hours. . . . The digestive organs, like a mill which is continually kept running, become enfeebled, vital force is called from the brain to aid the stomach in its overwork, and thus the mental powers are weakened. The unnatural stimulation and wear of the vital forces make the children nervous, impatient of restraint, self-willed, and irritable.— *H. R.*

197. They closely apply their minds to books, and **Students.** eat the allowance of the laboring man. Under such habits some grow corpulent, because the system is clogged. Others become lean, feeble, and weak, because their vital powers are exhausted in throwing off the excess of food.— *T.*, *V. III, p. 490.*

198. This is the way you treat the stomach. It is thoroughly exhausted, but instead of letting it rest, you give it more food, and then call the vitality from other parts of the system to the stomach to assist in the work of digestion.— *T.*, *V. II, p. 363.*

199. The poor tired stomach may complain of **Overworked** weariness in vain. More food is forced upon it, **Stomachs.** which sets the digestive organs in motion, again to perform the same round of labor through the sleep-

4

ing hours.   In the morning there is a sense of languor and loss of appetite; a lack of energy is felt
through the entire system.—*H. to L., Chap. 1, p. 55.*

200. And what influence does overeating have
upon the stomach? — It becomes debilitated, the
digestive organs are weakened, and disease, with
all its train of evils, is brought on as the result.   If
persons were diseased before, they thus increase the
difficulties upon them, and lessen their vitality every
day they live.   They call their vital powers into
unnecessary action to take care of the food that
they place in their stomachs.— *T., V. II, p. 364.*

201. Those who are excited, anxious, or in a great
hurry would do well not to eat until they have found
rest or relief, for the vital powers, already severely
taxed, cannot supply the necessary gastric juice.—
R. and H., 1884, No. 31.

**Improper
Clothing.**

202. She should not call vitality unnecessarily to
the surface to supply the want of sufficient clothing.
— *T., V. II, p. 382.*

**Rearing
Children.**

203. Everywhere you may look you will see pale,
sickly, care-worn, broken-down, dispirited, discouraged women.   They are generally overworked, and
their vital energies exhausted by frequent child-bearing.—*H. to L., Chap. 2, p. 31.*

204. Children who are robbed of that vitality which
they should have inherited from their parents should
have the utmost care.—*H. to L., Chap. 2, p. 59.*

Vice.

205. Secret indulgence is, in many cases, the only
real cause of the numerous complaints of the young.
This vice is laying waste the vital forces, and debilitating the system.—*S. A., pp. 57, 58.*

206. Sick people who take these drug poisons do **Drugs.** appear to get well. With some there is sufficient life force for nature to draw upon, so far to expel the poison from the system that the sick, having a period of rest, recover.— *H. to L., Chap. 3, p. 50.*

207. Some preserve a cold, chilling reserve, an **Unsocial Surroundings.** iron dignity, that repels those who are brought within their influence. This spirit is contagious, . . . it chokes the natural current of human sympathy, cordiality, and love ; and under its influence people become constrained, and their social and generous attributes are destroyed for want of exercise. Not only is the spiritual health affected, but the physical health suffers by this unnatural depression.— *T., V. IV, p. 64.*

208. The burden of sin, with its unrest and unsatisfied desires, lies at the very foundation of a large share of the maladies the sinner suffers.— *T., V. IV, p. 579.*

CHAPTER XI.

DISEASE AND PROVIDENCE.

209. The violation of physical law, and the consequence, human suffering, have so long prevailed that men and women look upon the present state of sickness, suffering, debility, and premature death as the appointed lot of humanity.— *T., V. III, p. 139.*

Disease the Result of Natural Causes.

210. Many persons complain of Providence because of the discomfort and inconvenience which they suffer, when this is the sure result of their own course. They seem to feel that they are ill-treated of God, when they themselves are alone responsible for the ills which they endure.—*R. and H., 1883, No. 41.*

211. Are these ills visited upon the race through God's providence?— No; they exist because the people have gone contrary to his providence, and still continue rashly to disregard his laws.— *R. and H., 1884, No. 31.*

212. The souls and bodies of people are fast becoming corrupted, a mass of disease. This would not have been the case if those who had claimed to believe the truth had lived out its sacred principles. —*U. T., Jan. 11, 1897.*

213. There is a divinely appointed connection between sin and disease. Sin and disease bear to each other the relationship of cause and effect.— *T. No. 32, p. 200.*

214. The course professed Christians generally pursue in following fashion, irrespective of health and life, brings upon them a train of evils which they charge back upon Providence, and place arguments in the mouths of infidels wherewith to assail Christianity.— *H. R.*

215. God is not responsible for the suffering which follows the non-conformity to natural law and moral obligations to him.— *H. R.*

216. Sickness and premature death do not come without a cause.— *H. to L., Chap. 4, p. 61.*

217. When standing by the graves of their children the afflicted parents look upon their bereavement as a special dispensation of Providence, when by inexcusable ignorance their own course has destroyed the lives of their children. To then charge their death to Providence, is blasphemy.— *T., V. III, p. 136.*

God not Responsible for Disease.

218. They should not charge the result of their own sinful course upon our gracious and merciful Heavenly Father. He doth not willingly afflict or grieve the children of men. — *H. R.*

219. Mothers are slow to learn that the suffering and death of their children is the result of their own course. They do not become intelligent upon the subject of how to live to prevent disease and premature death. What a thought! Mothers are the murderers of their own children, and are mourning over their death, and are trying hard to be reconciled to Providence, which they think has bereaved them.— *H. R.*

CHAPTER XII.

THE INFLUENCE OF DISEASE UPON THE MIND AND MORALS.

Mental Depression.

220. A diseased body affects the brain. With the mind we serve the Lord. — *F. of F.*, *p. 146*.

221. All should guard the senses, lest Satan gain victory over them; for these are the avenues to the soul. — *T.*, *V. III*, *p. 507*.

222. The brain nerves which communicate to the entire system are the only medium through which Heaven can communicate to man, and affect his inmost life. Whatever disturbs the circulation of the electric currents in the nervous system, lessens the strength of the vital powers, and the result is a deadening of the sensibilities of the mind. — *T.*, *V. II*, *p. 347*.

Moral Insensibility.

223. In consequence of the brain's being congested, its nerves lose their healthy action, and take on morbid conditions, making it almost impossible to arouse the moral sensibilities. — *H. R.*

224. It should ever be kept prominent that the great object to be attained through this channel is not only health, but perfection and the spirit of holiness, which cannot be attained with diseased bodies and minds. — *T.*, *V. I*, *p. 554*.

225. Mental and moral power is dependent upon the physical health. — *H. R.*

[54]

226. Physical and moral health are closely united. — *H. to L.*, *Chap.* *2, p. 32.*

227. The children of God cannot glorify him with sickly bodies or dwarfed minds. Those who indulge in any species of intemperance, either in eating or drinking, waste their physical energies and weaken moral power.— *C. T., p. 53.*

God Misrepresented.

228. Those whose moral faculties are beclouded by disease, are not the ones rightly to represent the Christian life, to show forth the joys of salvation or the beauties of holiness. They are too often in the fire of fanaticism or the water of cold indifference or stolid gloom.— *S. of T., 1885, No. 42.*

229. While men and women professing godliness are diseased from the crown of their head to the soles of their feet, while their physical, mental, and moral energies are enfeebled through gratification of depraved appetite and excessive labor, how can they weigh the evidences of truth, and comprehend the requirements of God? If their moral and intellectual faculties are beclouded, they cannot appreciate the value of the atonement or the exalted character of the work of God, nor delight in the study of his word. How can a nervous dyspeptic be ready always to give an answer to every man that asketh him for a reason of the hope that is in him, with meekness and fear?— *T., V. I, p. 488.*

230. Perfection and the spirit of holiness cannot be attained with diseased bodies and minds.— *T., V. I, p. 554.*

CHAPTER XIII.

HEREDITY.

Habits Repeated.

231. The physical and mental condition of parents is perpetuated in their offspring. This is a matter that is not duly considered. Wherever the habits of the parents are contrary to physical law, the injury done to themselves will be repeated in future generations. Satan knows this very well, and he is perpetuating his work through transmission. . . . Those who will indulge the animal passions and gratify lust will surely stamp upon their offspring the debasing practises, the grossness, of their own physical and moral defilement. By physical, mental, and moral culture all may become co-workers with Christ. Very much depends upon the parents. It lies with them whether they will bring into the world children who will prove a blessing or a curse.— *U. T., January, 1897.*

232. In past generations if mothers had informed themselves in regard to the laws of their being, they would have understood that their constitutional strength, as well as the tone of their morals and their mental faculties, would in a great measure be represented in their offspring.— *H. to L., Chap. 2, p. 37.*

233. He should not have committed so great a crime as to bring into being children that reason

must teach him would be diseased, because they must receive a miserable legacy from their parents. — *T., V. II, p. 379.*

234. As a rule every intemperate man who rears children transmits his inclinations and evil tendencies to his offspring ; he gives them disease from his own inflamed and corrupted blood. Licentiousness, disease, and imbecility are transmitted as an inheritance of woe from father to son, and from generation to generation, and this brings anguish and suffering into the world.— *T., V. IV, p. 30.* **Transmission of Disease.**

235. Thousands are devoid of principle. These very ones are transmitting to their offspring their own miserable, corrupt passions. What a legacy ! Thousands drag out their unprincipled lives, tainting their associates, and perpetuating their debased passions by transmitting them to their children.— *T., V. II, p. 351.*

236. You have transmitted to your children a miserable legacy ; a depraved nature rendered still more depraved by your gross habits of eating and drinking.— *T., V. II, p. 62.*

237. Parents sin not only against themselves in swallowing drug poisons, but they sin against their children. The vitiated state of the blood, the poison distributed throughout the system, the broken constitution, and various diseases, as the result of drug poisons, are transmitted to their offspring, and left to them a wretched inheritance, which is another great cause of the degeneracy of the race.— *H. to L., Chap. 3, p. 50.* **Parents Sin against Children.**

Mental and Moral Effects of Heredity.

238. Tobacco and liquor stupefy and defile the user. But the evil does not stop here. He transmits irritable tempers, polluted blood, enfeebled intellects, and weak morals to his children.—*T.*, *V. IV, p. 31.*

239. Those who have indulged the appetite for these stimulants have transmitted their depraved appetites and passions to their children, and greater moral power is required to resist intemperance in all its forms.—*T.*, *V. III, p. 488.*

240. As a rule, every intemperate man who rears children transmits his inclinations and evil tendencies to his offspring.— *T.*, *V. IV, p. 30.*

241. Parents who freely use wine and liquor leave to their children the legacy of a feeble constitution, mental and moral debility, unnatural appetites, irritable temper, and an inclination to vice. . . . The child of the drunkard or the tobacco inebriate usually has the depraved appetites and passions of the father intensified, and at the same time inherits less of his self-control and strength of mind.—*H. R.*

Physical Effects of Heredity.

242. Parents leave maladies as a legacy to their children.—*T.*, *V. IV, p. 30.*

243. Many women never should have become mothers. Their blood was filled with scrofula, transmitted to them from their parents, and increased by their gross manner of living.—*H. to L., Chap. 2, p. 37.*

244. Very many children are born with their blood tainted with scrofula through the wrong habits of the mother in her eating and dressing. . . . These fashionably dressed women cannot transmit good

constitutions to their children. . . . Wasp waists may have been transmitted to them from their mothers, as the result of their sinful practise of tight lacing, and in consequence of imperfect breathing. Poor children born of these miserable slaves of fashion have diminished vitality, and are predisposed to disease. . . . The impurities retained in the system in consequence of improper breathing are transmitted to their offspring.—*H. R.*

245. If the mother is deprived of an abundance of wholesome, nutritious food, she will lack in the quantity and quality of blood. Her circulation will be poor, and her child will lack in the very same things.— *T., V. II, p. 382.*

246. Her children were born with feeble digestive powers and impoverished blood. From the food the mother was compelled to receive, she could not furnish a good quality of blood, and therefore gave birth to children filled with humors.—*T., V. II, p. 378.*

247. Disease has been transmitted to your offspring, and the free use of flesh meats has increased the difficulty. The eating of pork has aroused and strengthened a most deadly humor that was in the system. Your offspring are robbed of vitality before they are born.— *T., V. II, p. 94.*

CHAPTER XIV.

CAUSES OF DISEASE.

Predisposing Causes.

248. Satan is the originator of disease. . . . There is a divinely appointed connection between sin and disease. . . . Sin and disease bear to each other the relationship of cause and effect.— *T., No. 32, p. 200.*

249. Disease never comes without a cause. The way is first prepared, and disease invited by disregarding the laws of health.— *H. to L., Chap. 5, p. 70.*

250. Sickness is caused by violating the laws of health.— *T., V. III, p. 164.*

251. The majority of diseases which the human family have been and are still suffering under, have been created by ignorance of their own organic law.— *H. R.*

Heredity. 252. Through disease transmitted to them from their parents, and an erroneous education in youth, they have imbibed wrong habits, injuring the constitution, affecting the brain, causing the moral organs to become diseased, and making it impossible for them to think and act rationally upon all points.— *R. and H., 1880, No. 11.*

253. Many are suffering in consequence of the transgressions of their parents; they cannot be cen-

sured for their parents sins, but it is nevertheless their duty to ascertain wherein their parents violated the laws of their being ; and wherein their parents' habits were wrong, they should change their course, and place themselves, by correct habits, in a better relation to health.— *II. R.*

254. The effects produced by living in close, ill-ventilated rooms are these : The system becomes weak and unhealthy, the circulation is depressed, the blood moves sluggishly through the system because it is not purified and vitalized by the pure, invigorating air of heaven. The mind becomes depressed and gloomy, while the whole system is enervated; and fevers and other acute diseases are liable to be generated. . . . The system is peculiarly sensitive to the influence of cold. A slight exposure produces serious diseases.— *T., V. I, p. 702.* **Impure Air.**

255. Stomach, liver, lungs, and brain are suffering for want of deep, full inspirations of air.— *T., V. II, p. 67.* **Imperfect Breathing.**

256. Close confinement indoors makes women pale and feeble, and results in premature death.— *H. R.* **Indoor Life.**

257. Indulging in eating too frequently, and in too large quantities, overtaxes the digestive organs, and produces a feverish state of the system. The blood becomes impure, and then diseases of various kinds occur.— *F. of F., p. 133.* **Improper Diet.**

258. The time women devote to studying how to prepare food in a manner to suit the perverted appetite is worse than lost ; . . . for they are only learning the most successful way to tear down and debase the physical, mental, and moral faculties

by gluttony. Then, as a natural result, comes sickness.— *H. R.*

259. I set before them the fact that by taking several kinds of food into the stomach at one meal, they are causing disease which was not attributed to the food eaten.— *U. T., Aug. 30, 1896.*

Overeating. 260. What influence does overeating have upon the stomach ?— It becomes debilitated, the digestive organs are weakened, and disease, with all its train of evils, is brought on as the result.— *T., V. II, p. 364.*

261. And the dyspeptic — what has made him dyspeptic is taking this course. Instead of observing regularity, he has let appetite control him, and has eaten between meals — *T., V. II, p. 374.*

262. They closely apply their minds to books, and eat the allowance of laboring men. . . . The liver becomes burdened, and unable to throw off the impurities of the blood, and sickness is the result.— *T., V. III, p. 490.*

263. Scanty, impoverished, ill-cooked food is constantly depraving the blood, by weakening the blood-making organs.— *T., V. I, p. 682.*

264. The free use of sugar in any form tends to clog the system, and is not unfrequently a cause of disease.— *C. T., p. 57.*

265. A great amount of milk and sugar . . . clog the system, irritate the digestive organs, and affect the brain.— *T., V. II, p. 370.*

Flesh Foods. 266. The liability to take disease is increased tenfold by meat eating.— *T., V. II, p. 64.*

267. The eating of flesh meats has made a poor quality of blood and flesh. Your systems are in a state of inflammation, prepared to take on disease. You are liable to acute attacks of disease, and to sudden death, because you do not possess the strength of constitution to rally and resist disease.— *T., V. II, p. 61.*

268. When we feed on flesh, the juices of what we eat pass into the circulation. A feverish condition is created, because the animals are diseased, and by partaking of their flesh, we plant the seeds of disease in our own tissue and blood. Then, when exposed to the changes in a malarious atmosphere, to prevailing epidemics and contagious diseases, these are more sensibly felt, for the system is not in a condition to resist disease.— *U. T., Nov. 5, 1896.*

269. Flesh meats constitute the principal article of food upon the tables of some families, until their blood is filled with cancerous and scrofulous humors. Their bodies are composed of what they eat. But when suffering and disease come upon them, it is considered an affliction of Providence.— *T., V. III, p. 563.*

270. Rich and complicated mixtures of food are health destroying. Highly seasoned meats and rich pastry are wearing out the digestive organs of children.— *U. T., Nov. 5, 1896.*

271. Simple grains, fruits, and vegetables have all the nutrient properties necessary to make good blood. This a flesh diet cannot do.— *U. T., Nov. 5, 1896.*

272. It is these hurtful stimulants that are surely **Stimulants.** undermining the constitution and preparing the

system for acute diseases, by impairing nature's fine machinery, and battering down her fortifications erected against disease and premature decay. — *T., V. I, p. 548.*

273. A tendency to disease of various kinds, as dropsy, liver complaint, trembling nerves, and a determination of the blood to the head, results from a habitual use of sour cider. By its use, many bring upon themselves permanent disease. Some die of consumption, or fall under the power of apoplexy from this cause alone. Some suffer from dyspepsia. Every vital function refuses to act, and the physicians tell them that they have liver complaint.— *R. and H., 1884, No. 13.*

Improper Clothing.

274. The fashionable style of woman's dress is one of the greatest causes of all these terrible diseases.— *H. R.*

275. More die as the result of following fashion than from all other causes.— *H. R.*

276. Women especially are the victims of various maladies which might be lessened, if not entirely prevented, by right habits of life. Half their sufferings may be attributed to their manner of dress, and the insane desire to conform to the fashions of the world.— *H. R.*

277. In order to follow the fashions, mothers dress their children with limbs nearly naked; and the blood is chilled back from its natural course and thrown upon the internal organs, breaking up the circulation and producing disease.— *T., V. II, p. 531.*

278. The chief, if not the only, reason why many become invalids is that the blood does not circulate freely, and the changes in the vital fluid, which are necessary to life and health, do not take place.— *T., V. II, p. 525.*

279. When we overtax our strength, and become exhausted, we are liable to take cold, and at such times there is danger of disease assuming a dangerous form.— *T., V. III, p. 13.* **Exposure to Cold.**

280. Rooms that are not exposed to light and air become damp. . . . Various diseases have been brought on by sleeping in these fashionable health-destroying apartments.— *H. to L., Chap. 4, p. 62.* **Damp Rooms.**

281. Disease never comes without a cause. The way is first prepared, and disease invited by disregarding the laws of health.— *H. to L., Chap. 5, p. 70.*

282. Drugging should be forever abandoned ; for while it does not cure any malady, it enfeebles the system, making it more susceptible to disease.— *T., No. 32, p. 67.* **Drugs.**

283. There is another class whose highest aim in life is physical labor. This class do not exercise the mind. Their muscles are exercised, while their brains are robbed of intellectual strength. . . . This class fall more readily if attacked by disease, because the system is not vitalized by the electrical force of the brain to resist disease.— *T., V. III, p. 157.* **The Condition of the Mind.**

284. That which brings sickness of body and mind to nearly all, is dissatisfied feelings and discontented repinings.— *T., V. I, p. 566.*

5

285. Nothing is so fruitful a cause of disease as depression, gloominess, and sadness.— *T., V. I, p. 702.*

Secret Vice.   286. This vice is laying waste the constitutions o very many, and preparing them for diseases of almost every description.— *S. A., p. 53.*

287. Some of nature's fine machinery gives way, leaving a heavier task for the remainder to perform, which disorders nature's fine arrangement, and there is often a sudden breaking down of the constitution ; and death is the result.— *S. A., p. 64.*

Exciting Causes.

Unhygienic Surroundings.   288. Filth is a breeder of disease.— *R. and H., 1896, No. 5.*

289. A neglect of cleanliness will induce disease. . . . Stubborn fevers and violent diseases have prevailed in neighborhoods and towns that had formerly been considered healthy, and some have died, while others have been left with broken constitutions to be crippled with disease for life. In many instances their own yards contained the agent of destruction, which sent forth deadly poisons into the atmosphere, to be inhaled by the family and the neighborhood.— *H. to L., Chap. 4, p. 61.*

290. Many suffer decayed vegetable matter to remain about their premises. They are not awake to the influence of these things. There is constantly arising from these decaying substances effluvium that is poisoning the air. By inhaling the impure air, the blood is poisoned, the lungs become affected, and the whole system is diseased. Disease of almost

every description will be caused by inhaling the atmosphere affected by these decaying substances.— *Ibid.*

291. If a house be built where water settles around it, remaining for a time and then drying away, a poisonous miasma arises, and fever and ague, sore throat, lung diseases, and fevers will be the result.— *H. to L., Chap. 4, p. 64.*

292. The mortality caused by eating meat is not discerned. . . . Animals are diseased, and by partaking of their flesh we plant the seeds of disease in our own tissues and blood.— *U. T., Nov. 5, 1896.* **Flesh Diet.**

293. The prevalence of cancers and tumors is largely due to gross living on dead flesh.— *U. T., Nov. 5, 1896.*

294. The practise of eating largely of meat is causing diseases of all kinds,— cancers, tumors, scrofula, tuberculosis, and numbers of other like affections.— *U. T., Jan. 11, 1897.*

295. Persons who live largely on a meat diet are in danger of putrefaction should they contract disease.— *U. T., Feb. 17, 1884.*

296. The eating of pork has aroused and strengthened a most deadly humor which was in the system. — *T, V. II, p. 94.*

CHAPTER XV.

RESISTANCE AGAINST DISEASE.

General Statements. 297. The object of the health reform and the Health Institute is not . . . to quiet the pains of to-day. No, indeed! Its great object is to teach the people how to live so as to give nature a chance to remove and resist disease.— *T., V. I, p. 643.*

298. The power of the human system to resist the abuses put upon it, is wonderful.— *R. and H., 1884, No. 4.*

299. A careful conformity to the laws which God has implanted in our being would insure health, and there would not be a breaking down of the constitution.— *H. R.*

300. A great amount of suffering might be saved if all would labor to prevent disease, by strictly obeying the laws of health.— *H. to L , Chap. 4, p. 60.*

The Power of the Will. 301. The power of the will is a mighty soother of the nerves, and can resist much disease, simply by not yielding to ailments and settling down into a state of inactivity.— *F. of F., p. 145.*

Temperance. 302. In order to preserve health, temperance in all things is necessary,— temperance in labor, temperance in eating and drinking.— *H. to L., Chap. 1, p. 57.*

Nourishment. 303. The body must have sufficient nourishment. The God who gives his beloved sleep has furnished them also suitable food to sustain the physical system in a healthy condition.— *C. T., p. 50.*

304. Nature will restore their vigor and strength in their sleeping hours, if her laws are not violated. — *S. A., p. 62.* **Sleep.**

305. Each faculty of the mind and each muscle has its distinctive office, and all require to be exercised in order to become properly developed and retain healthful vigor. Each organ and muscle has its work to do in the living organism. Every wheel in the machinery must be a living, active, working wheel. Nature's fine and wonderful works need to be kept in active motion in order to accomplish the object for which they were designed. Each faculty has a bearing upon the others, and all need to be exercised in order to be properly developed.— *T., V. III, p. 77.* **Exercise.**

306. Bathing frees the skin from the accumulation of impurities which are constantly collecting, and keeps the skin moist and supple, thereby increasing and equalizing the circulation. Persons in health should on no account neglect bathing. They should by all means bathe as often as twice a week.— *T., V. III, p. 70.* **Bathing.**

307. In order to maintain equal circulation, there should be an equal distribution of clothing, which will bring equal warmth to all parts of the body.— *H. R.* **Clothing.**

308. There is a much greater work upon us than we as yet have any idea of, if we would insure health by placing ourselves in the right relation to life. . . . The peculiar people whom God is purifying unto **Unselfish Work.**

himself, to be translated to heaven without seeing death, should not be behind others in good works. In their efforts to cleanse themselves from all filthiness of the flesh and spirit, perfecting holiness in the fear of God, they should be as far ahead of any other class of people on the earth as their profession is more exalted than that of others.— *T.*, *V. I*, *p. 487.*

309. Those who, so far as possible, engage in the work of doing good to others by giving practical demonstration of their interest in them, are not only relieving the ills of human life in helping them bear their burdens, but are at the same time contributing largely to their own health of soul and body. Doing good is a work that benefits both giver and receiver. If you forget self in your interest for others, you gain a victory over your infirmities. . . . The pleasure of doing good animates the mind and vibrates through the whole body.— *T.*, *V. II*, *p. 534.*

CHAPTER XVI.

VENTILATION.

General
Statements.

310. Air is the free blessing of heaven, calculated to electrify the whole system.— *T., V. I, p. 701.*

311. Air must be in constant circulation to be kept pure.— *T., V. I, p. 702.*

Ventilation
of the Sleep-
ing-Room.

312. Sleeping-rooms especially should be well ventilated, and the atmosphere made healthy by light and air. Blinds should be left open several hours each day, the curtains put aside, and the room thoroughly aired.— *H. to L., Chap. 4, p. 62.*

313. Sleeping apartments should be large, and so arranged as to have a circulation of air through them day and night. Those who have excluded the air from their sleeping-rooms should commence to change their course immediately. They should let in air by degrees, and increase its circulation until they can bear it winter and summer, with no danger of taking cold. The lungs, in order to be healthy, must have pure air.— *H. to L., Chap. 4, p. 63.*

Ventilation
in the Sick-
Room.

314. The sick-room, if possible, should have a draught of air through it day and night. The draught should not come directly upon the invalid. While burning fevers are raging, there is but little danger of taking cold. . . . The sick must have pure, invigorating air. If no other way can be devised, the sick, if possible, should be removed to

[71]

another room, and another bed, while the sick-room, the bed, and bedding are being purified by ventilation.— *H. to L., Chap. 4, p. 60.*

315. Every breath of vital air in the sick-room is of the greatest value, although many of the sick are very ignorant on this point. They feel much depressed, and do not know what the matter is. A draught of pure air through their room would have a happy, invigorating influence upon them.— *H. to L., Chap. 4, p. 59.*

Benefits of Pure Air.

316. Air, air, the precious boon of heaven, which all may have, will bless you with its invigorating influence if you will not refuse it entrance. Welcome it, cultivate a love for it, and it will prove a precious soother of the nerves. . . . The influence of pure, fresh air is to cause the blood to circulate healthfully through the system. It refreshes the body, and tends to render it strong and healthy, while at the same time its influence is decidedly felt upon the mind, imparting a degree of composure and serenity. It excites the appetite, and renders the digestion of food more perfect, and induces sound, sweet sleep.— *T., V. I, p. 702.*

Harmful Effects of Impure Air.

317. The harmful effects of living in close, ill-ventilated rooms are these : The system becomes weak and unhealthy; the circulation is depressed; the blood moves sluggishly through the system, because it is not purified and vitalized by the pure, invigorating air of heaven; the mind becomes depressed and gloomy, while the whole system is enervated, and fevers and other acute diseases are liable to be generated. — *T., V. I, p. 702.*

318. Many young children have passed five hours each day in schoolrooms not properly ventilated, nor sufficiently large for the healthful accommodation of the scholars. The air of such rooms soon becomes poison to the lungs that inhale it.— *T.*, *V. III, p. 135.*

319. Many families suffer with sore throat, lung diseases, and liver complaint, brought upon them by their own course of action. Their sleeping-rooms are small, unfit to sleep in for one night, but they occupy the small apartments for weeks, and months, and years. . . . They breathe the same air over and over, until it becomes inpregnated with the poisonous impurities and waste matter thrown off from their bodies through the lungs and the pores of the skin. . . . Those who thus abuse their health must suffer with disease.— *H. to L., Chap. 4, p. 63.*

CHAPTER XVII.

APPETITE.

320. Many are made sick by the indulgence of their appetite. They eat what suits their perverted taste, thus weakening the digestive organs, and injuring their power to assimilate the food that is to sustain life. . . . Thus the delicate machinery is worn out by the suicidal practises of those who ought to know better. Sin indeed lies at the door. The door is the mouth.— *U. T., Aug. 25, 1897.*

321. The declension in virtue and the degeneracy of the race are chiefly attributable to the indulgence of perverted appetite.— *T., V. III, p. 486.*

322. If the appetite is allowed to rule, the mind will be brought under its control.— *U. T., Jan. 11, 1897.*

323. One of the strongest temptations that man has to meet is upon the point of appetite.— *T., V. III, p. 485.*

324. As our first parents lost Eden through the indulgence of appetite, our only hope of regaining Eden is through the firm denial of appetite and passion. . . . The controlling power of appetite will prove the ruin of thousands, when, if they had conquered on this point, then they would have had the moral power to gain the victory over every other temptation of Satan. But those who are slaves to appetite will fail in perfecting Christian character.

. . . As we near the close of time, Satan's temptation to indulge appetite will be more powerful and
more difficult to overcome.— *T.*, *V. III, p. 491.*

325. Satan sees that he cannot have such a controlling power over us as he could if appetite were
indulged.— *T.*, *V. III, p. 569.*

326. Our habits of eating and drinking show
whether we are of the world or among the number
that the Lord by his .mighty cleaver of truth has
separated from the world.— *U. T., Aug. 25, 1897.*

327. Christ began this work of redemption by
reforming the physical habits of man.— *T.*, *V. III,
p. 486.*

328. In order for us to enjoy the natural appetite,
which will preserve health and prolong life, God
restricts the appetite. He says, Beware; restrain,
deny unnatural appetite.— *T.*, *V. III, p. 63.*

329. In its natural state, the taste might indicate,
in a great degree, the food best adapted to the
wants of the system. . . . This [the taste] might
be correct if the appetite had never been perverted.
There is a natural, and there is a depraved appetite.
— *H. R.*

CHAPTER XVIII.

DIET.

General Statements.
330. The diet question deserves careful study.— *Y. I., May 31, 1894.*

331. A reform in eating would be a saving of expense and labor.— *F. of F., p. 132.*

332. The diet affects both physical and moral health.— *C. T., p. 79.*

333. Learn for yourselves what you should eat, what kinds of food best nourish the body, and then follow the dictates of reason and conscience. This is not a matter of trifling importance.— *G. W., p. 174.*

334. Those who will not eat and drink from principle, will not be governed by principle in other things.— *H. R.*

Cooking.
335. The many dishes usually prepared for dessert should be dispensed with.— *U. T., Aug. 30, 1896.*

336. The large amount of cooking usually done is not at all necessary. Neither should the diet be poor, either in quality or quantity.— *U. T., Nov. 5, 1896.*

337. The proper cooking of food is a most essential requirement, especially where meat is not made an article of diet. Something must be prepared to take the place of meat, and these foods must be well

prepared, so that meat will not be desired.— *U. T.,
Dec. 20, 1897.*

338. We need persons who will educate themselves
to cook healthfully. Many know how to cook
meats and vegetables in different forms, yet do not
understand how to prepare simple and appetizing
dishes.— *Y. I., May 31, 1894.*

339. There is religion in good cooking, and I
question the religion of that class who are too ignorant and too careless to learn to cook.— *T., V. II,
p. 537.*

340. It is the positive duty of physicians to educate, educate, educate, by pen and voice, all who
have the responsibility of preparing food for the
table.— *U. T., Aug. 30, 1896.*

341. You profess to be health reformers, and for
this very reason you should become good cooks.
Those who can avail themselves of the advantages
of properly conducted hygienic cooking-schools, will
find it a great benefit, both in their own practise and
in teaching others. . . . One reason why many
have become discouraged in practising health reform
is that they have not learned how to cook so that
proper food, simply prepared, would supply the place
of the diet to which they have been accustomed.—
C. T., p. 119.

342. This [cooking] can be done in a simple,
healthful, and easy manner, without the use of lard,
butter, or flesh meats. . . . Skill must be united
with simplicity. To do this, women must read, and
then patiently reduce what they have read to practise.
Many are suffering because they will not take the

trouble to do this. . . . It is a religious duty for those who cook to learn how to prepare healthful food in different ways, so that it may be eaten with enjoyment. . . . What branch of the education of a young lady can be so important as this ? — *T.*, *V. I, pp. 681, 682.*

Proper Food.   343. Is my diet such as will bring me in a position where I can accomplish the greatest amount of good ? — *R. and H., 1880, No. 25.*

344. People cannot all eat the same things. Some articles of food that are wholesome and palatable to one person may be hurtful to another. So it is impossible to make an unvarying rule by which to regulate every one's dietetic habits.— *C. T., p. 157.*

345. The Lord intends to bring his people back to live upon simple fruits, vegetables, and grains. . . . God provided fruit in its natural state for our first parents.— *U. T., Nov. 5, 1896.*

346. All the elements of nutrition are contained in the fruits, vegetables, and grains.— *R. and H., 1883, No. 19.*

347. Grains and fruits prepared free from grease, and in as natural a condition as possible, should be the food for the tables of all who claim to be preparing for translation to heaven.— *T., V. II, p. 352.*

348. Fruits, grains, and vegetables, prepared in a simple way, free from spice and grease of all kinds, make, with milk and cream, the most healthful diet. They impart nourishment to the body, and give a power of endurance and vigor of intellect that are not produced by a stimulating diet.— *C. T., p. 47.*

349. Meat eating is doing its work, for the meat is diseased. We may not long be able to use even milk.— *U. T.*, *Aug. 30, 1896.*

350. Good, ripe, undecayed fruit is a thing for which we should thank the Lord, for it is beneficial to health.— *U. T.*, *Nov. 5, 1896.*

351. Dry food which requires mastication is far preferable to porridges. The health food preparations are a blessing in this respect.— *U. T.*, *Jan. 11, 1897.*

352. My sisters, do not place upon your tables food that is exciting and irritating, but that which is plain, wholesome, and nutritious.—*R. and H.*, *1884, No. 31.*

353. Good brown bread and rolls, prepared in a simple manner, yet with painstaking effort, are healthful.— *U. T.*, *Jan. 11, 1897.*

Preparation of Food.

354. In the preparation of food, the golden rays of light are to be kept shining, teaching those who sit at the table how to live.— *U. T.*, *Aug. 12, 1896.*

355. Food should be thoroughly cooked, nicely prepared, and appetizing.— *U. T.*, *Nov. 5, 1896.*

356. The food should have been prepared in a simple form, and free from grease; but pains should have been taken to have it nutritious, healthful, and inviting.— *T.*, *V. II, p. 485.*

Palatability.

357. Food should be prepared with simplicity, and yet with a nicety that will invite the appetite.— *T.*, *V. II, p. 63.*

358. Great care should be taken when the change is made from a flesh meat to a vegetarian diet, to supply the table with wisely prepared, well-cooked articles of food.— *U. T., Jan. 11, 1897.*

359. It is important that the food should be prepared with care, that the appetite, when not perverted, may relish it.— *T., V. II, p. 367.*

360. Unless the food is prepared in a wholesome, palatable manner, it cannot be converted into good blood, to build up the wasting tissues. — *T., V. II, p. 538.*

361. Many do not feel that this is a matter of duty, and hence they do not try to prepare food properly. This can be done in a simple, healthful, and easy manner, without the use of lard, butter, or flesh meats.— *T., V. I, p. 681.*

362. In every line of cooking the question which should be considered, is, How can the food be prepared in the most natural and inexpensive manner? And there should be careful study that the fragments of food left over from the table be not wasted.— *U. T., Jan. 11, 1897.*

Bread   363. Hot raised bread of any kind is difficult of digestion.—*R. and H., 1883, No. 19.*

364. Bread should never have the slightest taint of sourness. It should be cooked until it is most thoroughly done. Thus all softness and stickiness will be avoided. . . . Milk should not be used in place of water in bread making. All this is extra expense, and is not wholesome. If the bread thus made is allowed to stand over in warm weather, and is then broken open, there will frequently be seen

long strings like cobwebs. Such bread soon causes fermentation to take place in the stomach. . . . Every housekeeper should feel it her duty to educate herself to make good sweet bread in the most inexpensive manner, and the family should refuse to have upon the table bread that is heavy and sour, for it is injurious.— *U. T., Jan. 11, 1897.*

365. Hot biscuit raised with soda or baking-powder should never appear upon our tables. Such compounds are unfit to enter the stomach.—*R. and H., 1883, No. 19.*

366. Saleratus in any form should not be introduced into the stomach; for the effect is fearful. It eats the coatings of the stomach, causes inflammation, and frequently poisons the entire system. Some plead, "I cannot make good bread and gems unless I use soda or saleratus." You surely can if you will learn. Is not the health of your family of sufficient value to inspire you with ambition to learn how to cook and how to eat?— *T., V. II, p. 537.*

367. There should not be many kinds at any one Variety. meal, but all meals should not be composed of the same kinds of food without variation.— *T., V. II, p. 63.*

368. I set before them the fact that by placing several kinds of food in the stomach at one meal, they were causing disease that was not attributed to the food eaten.— *U. T., Aug. 30, 1896.*

369. If your work is sedentary, take exercise every day, and at each meal eat only two or three kinds of simple food, taking no more of these than will satisfy the demands of hunger.— *U. T., Aug. 30, 1896.*

370. It would be better to eat only two or three different kinds of food at each meal than to load the stomach with many varieties.— *U. T., Aug. 30, 1896.*

371. Do not have too great a variety at a meal; three or four dishes are a plenty. At the next meal you can have a change. The cook should tax her inventive powers to vary the dishes she prepares for the table, and the stomach should not be compelled to take the same kinds of food meal after meal.— *R. and H., 1884, No. 31.*

372. Some think that they must eat only just such .an amount, and just such a quality, and confine themselves to two or three kinds of food. But in eating too small an amount, and that not of the best quality, they do not receive sufficient nourishment. — *C. T., p. 57.*

Food Com-
binations.
373. Mixed and complicated dishes are injurious to the health of human beings.— *U. T., Nov. 5, 1896.*

374. It is not well to take a great variety of food at one meal. When a variety of foods that do not agree are crowded into the stomach at one meal, what can we expect but that a disturbance will be created?— *U. T., Jan. 11, 1897.*

375. I advise the people to give up sweet puddings or custards made with eggs and milk and sugar, and to eat the best home-made bread, both graham and white, with dried or green fruits, and let that be the only course for one meal ; then let the next meal be of nicely prepared vegetables.—*U. T., Oct. 29, 1894.*

376. If we would preserve the best health, we should avoid eating vegetables and fruit at the same meal. If the stomach is feeble, there will be distress, and the brain will be confused, and unable to put forth mental effort. Have fruit at one meal and vegetables at the next.— *Y. I., May 31, 1894.*

377. We advise you to change your habits of living; but while you do this, we caution you to move understandingly. · I am acquainted with families who have changed from a meat diet to one that is impoverished. Their food is so poorly prepared that the stomach loathes it. . . . Here is one reason why some have not been successful in their efforts to simplify their food.— *T., V. II, p. 63.*

378. Large quantities of milk and sugar eaten together are injurious.— *T., V. II, p. 369.*

379. Some use milk and a large amount of sugar on mush, thinking that they are carrying out health reform. But the sugar and the milk combined are liable to cause fermentation in the stomach, and are thus harmful. The free use of sugar in any form tends to clog the system, and is not unfrequently a cause of disease.— *C. T., p. 57.*

380. Rich and complicated mixtures of food are health destroying.— *U. T., Nov. 5, 1896.*

381. The stomach must have careful attention. **Number of Meals.** . . . After it has done its work for one meal, do not crowd more work upon it before it has had a chance to rest, and before a sufficient supply of gastric juice is provided. Five hours at least should be given between each meal, and always bear in mind that if you would give it a trial, you

would find two meals better than three.— *U. T.,
Aug. 30, 1896.*

382. A second meal should never be eaten until
the stomach has had time to rest from the labor of
digesting the preceding meal.— *H. to L., Chap. 1,
p. 55.*

383. It is quite a common custom with the people
of the world to eat three times a day, besides eating
at irregular intervals between meals; and the last
meal is generally the most hearty, and is often taken
just before retiring. This is reversing the natural
order; a hearty meal should never be taken so late in
the day. Should these persons change their practise,
and eat but two meals a day, and nothing between
meals, not even an apple, a nut, or any kind of
fruit, the result would be seen in a good appetite
and greatly improved health.— *R. and H., 1884,
No. 31.*

384. Most people enjoy better health while eating
two meals a day than three; others, under their ex-
isting circumstances, may require something to eat
at supper time; but this meal should be very light.
Let no one think himself a criterion for all, that
every one must do exactly as he does.— *C. T., p. 58.*

385. If the third meal be eaten at all, it should
be light, and several hours before going to bed.—
H. to L., Chap. 1, p. 55.

386. The stomach, when we lie down to rest,
should have its work all done, that it may enjoy
rest, as well as other portions of the body. The
work of digestion should not be carried on through

any period of the sleeping hours.— *H. to L.*, *Chap. 1, p. 56.*

387. If you feel that you must eat at night, take a drink of cold water, and in the morning you will feel much better for not having eaten.— *T., V. IV, p. 502.*

388. The stomach may be educated to desire food eight times a day, and feel faint if it is not supplied. But this is no argument in favor of so frequent eating.— *R. and H., 1883, No. 19.*

Errors in Diet.

389. At meal-time cast off care and taxing thought. Do not be hurried, but eat slowly and with cheerfulness, your heart filled with gratitude to God for all his blessings.— *G. W., p. 174.*

Condition of the Mind at Meals.

390. If you are in constant fear that your food will hurt you, it most assuredly will.— *T., V. II, p. 530.*

391. Some health reformers are constantly worrying for fear their food, however simple and healthful, will hurt them. To these let me say, Do not think that your food is going to hurt you; but when you have eaten according to your best judgment, and have asked the Lord to bless the food, believe that he has heard your prayer, and be at rest.— *C. T., p 59.*

392. You should never let a morsel pass your lips between your regular meals. Eat what you ought, but eat it at one meal, and then wait until the next. — *T., V. II, p. 373.*

Eating between Meals.

393. Three meals a day and nothing between meals — not even an apple — should be the utmost limit of indulgence. Those who go further violate nature's laws and will suffer the penalty.— *R. and H., 1883, No. 19.*

394. When traveling, some are almost constantly nibbling, if there is anything within their reach. This is a most pernicious practise. Animals that do not have reason, and that know nothing of mental taxation, may do this without injury, but they are no criterion for rational beings, who have mental powers that should be used for God and humanity.— *R. and H., 1884, No. 31.*

395. Food taken into the stomach at untimely seasons leaves an influence on every fiber of the system.— *H. R*

Hasty Eating.

396. In order to have healthy digestion, food should be eaten slowly. Those who wish to avoid dyspepsia, and those who realize the obligation to keep all their powers in a condition which will enable them to render the best service to God, will do well to remember this. If your time to eat is limited, do not bolt your food, but eat less, and eat slowly.— *R. and H., 1884, No. 31.*

397. Do not be hurried, but eat slowly and with cheerfulness, your heart filled with gratitude to God for all his blessings.— *G. W., p. 174.*

398. Eat slowly, and allow the saliva to mingle with the food. The more liquid there is taken into the stomach with the meals, the more difficult it is for the food to digest. . . . The benefit you derive from your food does not depend so much on the

quantity eaten, as on its thorough digestion, nor the gratification of the taste so much on the amount of food swallowed as on the length of time it remains in the mouth.— *R. and H., 1884, No. 31.*

399. If more food is eaten than can be digested **Overeating.** and appropriated, a decaying mass accumulates in the stomach, causing an offensive breath, and a bad taste in the mouth. The vital powers are exhausted in an effort to throw off the excess, and the brain is robbed of nerve force.— *S. T. on E., p. 32.*

400. Nearly all the members of the human family eat more than the system requires. . . . Even so-called health reform needs reforming on this point. . . . If more food, even of a simple quality, is placed in the stomach than the living machinery requires, this surplus becomes a burden, the system makes a desperate effort to dispose of it, and this extra work causes a weakly feeling. Some who are continually overeating call this all-gone feeling hunger, but it is caused by the overworked condition of the abused digestive organs.— *U. T., Aug. 30, 1896.*

401. Some of you feel as though you would like to have somebody tell you how much to eat. This is not the way it should be. We are to act from a moral and religious standpoint. We are to be temperate in all things, because an incorruptible crown, a heavenly treasure, is before us. And now I wish to say to my brethren and sisters, I would have moral courage to take my position and govern myself. You eat too much, and then you are sorry, and so you keep thinking upon what you eat and drink. Just eat that which is for the best, and go

right away, feeling clear in the sight of Heaven, and not having remorse of conscience.— *T.*, *V. II*, *p. 374.*

402. There is evil in overeating of even healthful food. . . . If we overeat, the brain power is taxed to take care of a large quantity of food that the system does not demand, the mind is clouded, and the perceptions enfeebled.— *U. T.*, *April 6, 1896.*

403. When the brain is constantly taxed, and there is a lack of physical exercise, they should eat sparingly, even of plain food.— *T.*, *V. IV*, *p. 515.*

404. They closely apply their minds to books, and eat the allowance of a laboring man. Under such habits some grow corpulent, because the system is clogged. Others become lean, feeble, and weak, because their vital powers are exhausted in throwing off the excess of food ; the liver becomes burdened, and unable to throw off the impurities in the blood, and sickness is the result.— *T.*, *V. III*, *p. 490.*

405. Overeating, even of the simplest food, benumbs the sensitive nerves of the brain, and weakens its vitality. Overeating has a worse effect upon the system than overworking; the energies of the soul are more effectually prostrated by intemperate eating than by intemperate working. The digestive organs should never be burdened with the quantity or quality of food which it will tax the system to appropriate. All that is taken into the stomach, above what the system can use to convert into good blood, clogs the machinery ; for it cannot be made into either flesh or blood, and its presence burdens the

liver, and produces a morbid condition of the system.— *T., V. II, p. 412.*

406. Overeating is intemperance just as surely as is liquor drinking.— *U. T., Aug. 30, 1896.*

407. And what influence does overeating have upon the stomach? — It becomes debilitated, the digestive organs are weakened, and disease, with all its train of evils, is brought on as the result. If persons were diseased before, they thus increase the difficulties upon them, and lessen their vitality every day they live. They call their vital powers into unnecessary action to take care of the food that they place in their stomachs. What a terrible condition is this to be in! — *T., V. II, p. 364.*

408. Eating merely to please the appetite is a transgression of nature's laws; often this intemperance is felt at once in the form of indigestion, headache, and colic. A load has been placed upon the stomach that it cannot care for, and a feeling of oppression comes. The head is confused, the stomach is in rebellion. But these results do not always follow overeating. In some cases the stomach is paralyzed. No sensation of pain is felt, but the digestive organs lose their vital force. The foundation of the human machinery is gradually undermined, and life is rendered very unpleasant.— *U. T., Aug. 30, 1896.*

409. Taken with meals, water diminishes the flow of the salivary glands; and the colder the water the greater the injury to the stomach. Ice water or iced lemonade, drunk with meals, will arrest digestion until the system has imparted sufficient warmth

Drinking at Meals.

to the stomach to enable it to take up its work
again.— *R. and H., 1884, No. 31.*

410. Food should not be washed down; no drink
is needed with meals. Eat slowly, and allow the
saliva to mingle with the food. The more liquid
there is taken into the stomach with the meals, the
more difficult it is for the food to digest; for the
liquid must be first absorbed. . . . Hot drinks are
debilitating; and besides, those who indulge in their
use become slaves to the habit. . . . Do not eat
largely of salt; give up bottled pickles; keep fiery
spiced food out of your stomach; eat fruit with your
meals, and the irritation which calls for so much
drink will cease to exist. But if anything is needed
to quench thirst, pure water, drunk some little time
before or after a meal, is all that nature requires.
. . . Water is the best liquid possible to cleanse
the tissues.— *R. and H., 1884, No. 31.*

**Liquid
Foods.**
411. I am advising the people wherever I go to
give up liquid food as much as possible.— *U. T.,
Oct. 29, 1894.*

412. Taken in a liquid state, your food would not
give healthful vigor or tone to the system. But
when you change this habit, and eat more solids
and less liquids, your stomach will feel disturbed.
Notwithstanding this, you should not yield the point,
you should educate your stomach to bear a more
solid diet.— *T., V. III, p. 74.*

413. Dry food that requires mastication is far
preferable to porridges. The health food preparations are a blessing in this respect. . . . For those
who can use them, good vegetables, prepared in a

healthful manner, are better than soft mushes and porridge. Fruits, used with thoroughly cooked bread two or three days old, which is more healthful than fresh bread, slowly and thoroughly masticated, will furnish all that the system requires.— *U. T., Jan. 11, 1897.*

414. Very hot food ought not to be taken into the stomach. Soups, puddings, and other articles of the kind, are often eaten too hot, and as a consequence the stomach is debilitated. Let them become partly cooled before they are eaten.— *R. and H., 1884, No. 31.* **Very Hot Foods.**

415. I do not approve of eating much cold food, for the reason that the vitality must be drawn from the system to warm the food until it becomes of the same temperature as the stomach before the work of digestion can be carried on.— *T., V. II, p. 603.* **Cold Food.**

416. Rich and complicated mixtures of food are health destroying. Highly seasoned meats and rich pastry are wearing out the digestive organs of children.— *U. T., Nov. 5, 1896.* **Rich Diet.**

417. At too many tables, when the stomach has received all that it requires to carry on the work of nourishing the system, another course, consisting of pies, puddings, and highly flavored sauces, is placed upon the table. . . . Many, though they have already eaten enough, will overstep the bounds, and eat the tempting dessert, which, however, proves anything but good to them. . . . If the extras which are provided for dessert were dispensed with altogether, it would be a blessing.— *U. T., Aug. 30, 1896.*

418. Many understand how to make different kinds of cakes, but cake is not the best food to be placed upon the table. Sweet cakes, sweet puddings, and custards will disorder the digestive organs; and why should we tempt those who surround the table by placing such articles before them? — *Y. I., May 31, 1894.*

419. Cook meat with spices, and eat it with rich cakes and pies, and you have a bad quality of blood. The system is too heavily taxed in disposing of this kind of food. The mince pies and pickles, which should never find a place in any human stomach, will give a miserable quality of blood. . . . Flesh meat and rich food and an impoverished diet will produce the same results.— *T., V. II, p. 368.*

Condiments.

420. Condiments and spices, used in the preparation of food for the table, aid digestion in the same way that tea, coffee, and liquor are supposed to help the laboring man to perform his task. After the immediate effects are gone, those who use them drop as far below par as they were elevated above par by these stimulating substances. The system is weakened, the blood contaminated, and inflammation is the sure result. The less frequently condiments and desserts are placed on our tables, the better it will be for all who partake of the food.— *U. T., Nov. 5, 1896.*

421. Our tables should bear only the most wholesome food, free from every irritating substance. The appetite for liquor is encouraged by the preparation of food with condiments and spices. These cause a feverish state of the system, and drink is demanded

to allay the irritation. On my frequent journeys across the continent, I do not patronize restaurants, dining-cars, or hotels, for the simple reason that I cannot eat the food there provided. The dishes are highly seasoned with salt and pepper, creating an almost intolerable thirst. . . . They irritate and inflame the delicate coating of the stomach. . . . Such is the food that is commonly served upon fashionable tables, and given to the children. Its effect is to cause nervousness, and to create thirst which water does not quench. . . . Food should be prepared in as simple a manner as possible, free from condiments and spices, and even from an undue amount of salt.— *R. and H., 1883, No. 44.*

422. Spices at first irritate the tender coating of **Spices.** the stomach, but finally destroy the natural sensitiveness of this delicate membrane. The blood becomes fevered, the animal propensities are aroused, while the moral and intellectual powers are weakened, and become servants to the baser passions.— *C. T., p. 47.*

423. Persons who have indulged their appetite to eat freely of meat, highly seasoned gravies, and various kinds of rich cakes and preserves, cannot immediately relish a plain, wholesome, nutritious diet. Their taste is so perverted they have no appetite for a wholesome diet of fruits, plain bread, and vegetables. They need not expect to relish at first food so different from that in which they have been indulging. If they cannot at first enjoy plain food, they should fast until they can. That fast will prove to them of greater benefit than medicine, for the abused stomach will find the rest which it has

long needed, and real hunger can be satisfied with a plain diet. It will take time for the taste to recover from the abuses it has received, and to gain its natural tone. But perseverance in a self-denying course of eating and drinking will soon make plain, wholesome food palatable, and it will be eaten with greater satisfaction than the epicure enjoys over his rich dainties.— *F. of F., p. 130.*

Cheese.

424. The effect of cheese is deleterious.— *C. T., p. 47.*

425. Cheese should never be introduced into the stomach.— *T., V. II, p. 68.*

Grease, fats, etc.

426. Meat is served reeking with fat, because it suits the perverted taste. Both the blood and the fat of animals is consumed as a luxury. But the Lord has given special directions that these should not be eaten. Why?— Because their use would make a diseased current of blood in the human system. Disregard of the Lord's special directions has brought many diseases upon human beings.— *U. T., March, 1896.*

427. Jesus, speaking of the cloudy pillar, gave special direction to the children of Israel, saying : " It shall be a perpetual statute for your generations throughout all your dwellings, that ye eat neither fat nor blood." "And the Lord spake unto Moses, saying, Speak unto the children of Israel, saying, Ye shall eat no manner of fat, of ox, of sheep, or of goat." " For whosoever eateth the fat of the beasts, of which men offer an offering made by fire unto the Lord, even the soul that eateth it shall

be cut off from among his people."— *U. T.,
March, 1897.*

428. You should keep grease out of your food.
It defiles any preparation of food you may make.—
T., V. II, p. 63.

429. Grease cooked in the food renders it difficult
of digestion.— *C. T., p. 47.*

430. Some fall into the error that because they
discard meat, they have no need to supply its place
with the best fruits and vegetables, prepared in their
most natural state, free from grease and spices.—
T., V. II, p. 486.

431. Butter and meat stimulate. They have in
jured the stomach and perverted the taste.— *T.,
V. II, p. 486.*

432. You place upon your tables butter, eggs, and
meat, and your children partake of them. They are
fed with the very things that will excite their animal
passions, and then you come to meeting and ask
God to bless and save your children.— *T., V. II,
p. 362.*

433. Saleratus in any form should not be introduced into the stomach; for the effect is fearful. It
eats the coatings of the stomach, causes inflammation, and frequently poisons the entire system.— *T.,
V. II, p. 537.*

Saleratus and Soda.

434. Hot soda biscuit are often spread with butter,
and eaten as a choice diet; but the feeble digestive
organs cannot but feel the abuse placed upon them.
— *U. T., Nov. 5, 1896.*

CHAPTER XIX.

FLESH FOODS.

General
Statements. 435. Meat is not essential for health or strength, else the Lord made a mistake when he provided food for Adam and Eve before their fall. All the elements of nutrition are contained in the fruits, vegetables, and grains.—*R. and H., 1883, No. 19.*

The Ideal
Diet. 436. The Lord intends to bring his people back to live upon simple fruits, vegetables, and grains. He led the children of Israel into the wilderness where they could not get a flesh diet; and he gave them the bread of heaven. "Man did eat angels' food." But they craved the flesh-pots of Egypt, and mourned and cried for flesh, notwithstanding the promise of the Lord that if they would submit to his will, he would carry them into the land of Canaan, and establish them there, a pure, holy, happy people, and that there should not be a feeble one in all their tribes; for he would take away all sickness from among them. . . . The Lord would have given them flesh had it been essential for their health, but he who had created and redeemed them led them through that long journey in the wilderness to educate, discipline, and train them in correct habits. The Lord understood what influence flesh eating has upon the human system. He would have a people that would, in their physical appearance,

[96]

bear the divine credentials, notwithstanding their long journey.— *U. T., Nov. 5, 1896.*

437. When the selfishness of taking the lives of animals to gratify a perverted appetite was presented to me by a Catholic woman, I felt ashamed and distressed. I saw it in a new light, and I said, I will no longer patronize the butcher, I will not have the flesh of slain animals on my table.— *U. T., Aug. 30, 1896.*

438. The diet of animals is vegetables and grains. Must the vegetables be animalized, must they be incorporated into the system of an animal, before we get them? Must we obtain our vegetable diet by eating the flesh of dead creatures? God provided food in its natural state for our first parents. He gave Adam charge of the garden, to dress it and to care for it, saying, "To you it shall be for meat." One animal was not to destroy another animal for food.— *U. T., Nov. 5, 1896.*

439. Those who have lived upon a meat diet all their lives do not see the evil of continuing the practise, and they must be treated tenderly.— *U. T., June 19, 1895.*

440. Something must be prepared to take the place of meat, and these foods must be well prepared, so that meat will not be desired.— *U. T., Dec. 20, 1896.*

Substitutes for Meat.

441. I know that with care and skill, dishes could be prepared to take the place of meat. But if the main dependence of the cook is meat, she will encourage meat eating, and the depraved appetite

7

will frame every excuse for this kind of diet.—
U. T., Feb. 14, 1884.

442. Meat is the most expensive diet that can be
had.— *U. T., Feb. 17, 1884.*

Effects of Meat Eating.

**Physical
Effects.**
443. We do not hesitate to say that flesh meat is
not necessary for health or strength.— *T., Vol. II,
p. 63.*

444. One of the great errors that many insist upon
is that muscular strength is dependent upon animal
food. But the simple grains, fruits of the trees,
and vegetables have all the nutritive properties
necessary to make good blood. This a flesh diet
cannot do.— *U. T., Nov. 5, 1896.*

445. Speaking in support of this diet, they said
that without it they were weak in physical strength.
But the words of our Teacher to us were, "As a man
thinketh, so is he." The flesh of dead animals was
not the original food for man. Man was permitted
to eat it after the flood, because all vegetation had
been destroyed. . . . Since the flood the human
race has been shortening the period of its existence.
Physical, mental, and moral degeneracy is rapidly
increasing in these last days.— *U. T., Jan. 11, 1897.*

446. The weakness experienced on leaving off meat
is one of the strongest arguments that I could present
as a reason why you should discontinue its use.
Those who eat meat feel stimulated after eating this
food, and they suppose that they are made stronger.
After they discontinue the use of meat, they may
for a time feel weak, but when the system is cleansed

from the effect of this diet, they no longer feel the weakness, and will cease to wish for that for which they have pleaded as essential to strength.— *U. T., Aug. 30, 1896.*

447. You may think that you cannot work without meat; I thought so once, but I know that in his original plan God did not provide for the use of the flesh of dead animals as a diet for man. It is a gross, perverted taste .that will accept such food. To think of dead flesh rotting in the stomach is revolting.— *U. T., Feb. 17, 1884.*

448. The eating of flesh meats has made a poor quality of blood and flesh. Your systems are in a state of inflammation, prepared to take on disease. You are liable to acute attacks of disease, and to sudden death, because you do not possess the strength of constitution to rally and resist disease. — *T., V. II, p. 61.*

449. The physical powers are depreciated by the habitual use of flesh meat. Meat eating deranges the system.— *T., Vol. II, p. 64.*

450. The use of the flesh of animals tends to cause a grossness of the body.— *T., V. II, p. 63.*

451. Their meat diet, which was supposed to be essential, was not necessary, and as they were composed of what they ate, brain, bone, and muscle were in an unwholesome condition because they lived on the flesh of dead animals. Their blood was being corrupted by this improper diet. The flesh which they ate was diseased, and their entire system was becoming gross and corrupted.— *U. T., Aug. 30, 1896.*

452. When we feed on flesh, the juices of what we eat pass into the circulation. A feverish condition is created, because the animals are diseased, and by partaking of their flesh we plant the seeds of disease in our own tissue and blood. Then, when exposed to the changes of a malarious atmosphere, to prevailing epidemics and contagious diseases, these are more sensibly felt, for the system is not in a condition to resist disease.— *U. T., Nov. 5, 1896.*

453. Because those who partake of animal food do not immediately feel its effects, is no evidence that it does not injure them. It may be doing its work surely upon the system, and yet the persons for the time being realize nothing of it.— *H. to L., Chap. 1, p. 59.*

454. The liability to take disease is increased tenfold by meat eating.— *T., V. II, p. 64.*

455. The practise of eating largely of meat is causing diseases of all kinds,— cancers, tumors, scrofula, tuberculosis, and other like affections.— *U. T., Jan. 11, 1897.*

456. The mortality caused by meat eating is not discerned. If it were, we should hear no arguments and excuses in favor of the indulgence of the appetite for dead flesh.— *U. T., Nov. 5, 1896.*

457. Her system is full of scrofulous humors from the eating of flesh meats. The use of swine's flesh in your family has imparted a bad quality of blood. — *T., V. II, p. 62.*

458. Cancers, tumors, and various other inflammatory diseases are largely caused by meat eating.

From the light which God has given me, the prevalence of cancers and tumors is largely due to gross living on dead flesh.— *U. T.*, *Nov. 5, 1896*.

459. Persons who live largely on a meat diet are in danger of putrefaction should they contract disease.— *U. T.*, *Feb. 17, 1884*.

460. When a limb is broken, physicians recommend their patients not to eat meat, as there would be danger of inflammation's setting in.— *U. T.*, *Nov. 5, 1896*.

461. If we subsist largely upon the flesh of dead animals, we shall partake of their nature.— *T.*, *V. II, p. 61*. **Mental and Moral Effects.**

462. A meat diet changes the disposition, and strengthens animalism. . . . To educate your children to subsist on a meat diet would be harmful to them.— *U. T.*, *Nov. 5, 1896*.

463. Its use excites the animal propensities to increased activity, and strengthens the animal passions. When the animal propensities are increased, the intellectual and moral powers are decreased. The use of the flesh of animals . . . benumbs the fine sensibilities of the mind.— *T.*, *V. II, p. 63*.

464. It is impossible for those who make free use of flesh meats to have an unclouded brain and an active intellect.— *T.*, *V. II, p. 62*.

465. Eating much flesh will diminish intellectual activity. Students would accomplish much more in their studies if they never tasted meat. When the animal part of the human nature is strengthened by meat eating, the intellectual powers diminish proportionately.— *U. T.*, *Nov. 5, 1896*.

466. Meat eating deranges the system, beclouds the intellect, and blunts the moral sensibilities.— *T., V. II, p. 64.*

467. Such a diet contaminates the blood and stimulates the lower passions. It prevents vigor of thought and enfeebles the perceptions, so that God and the truth are not understood.— *U. T., Jan. 11, 1897.*

Spiritual Effects.

468. O, if every one could discern these matters as they have been presented to me, those who are so careless, so indifferent in regard to their character building, those who plead for indulgence in a flesh-meat diet, would never open their lips in justification of an appetite for the flesh of dead animals.— *U. T., Jan. 11, 1897.*

469. A religious life can be more successfully attained and maintained if meat is discarded; for this diet stimulates into intense activity the lustful propensities, and enfeebles the moral and spiritual nature.— *U. T., Nov. 5, 1896.*

Diseased Meats.

470. The meat diet is a serious question. Shall human beings live on the flesh of dead animals? The answer, from the light that God has given, is, No, decidedly no. Our health institutions should educate on this question. . . . They should point out the increase of disease in the animal kingdom. The testimony of examiners is that very few animals are free from disease.— *U. T., Jan. 11, 1897.*

471. Disease of every type is afflicting the human family, and it is largely the result of subsisting on the diseased flesh of dead animals.— *U. T., March, 1896.*

472. Those who subsist largely upon flesh cannot avoid eating the meat of animals which are to a greater or less degree diseased. The process of fitting the animals for market produces in them disease; and fitted in as healthful a manner as they can be, they become heated and diseased by driving before they reach the market. The fluids and flesh of these diseased animals are received directly into the blood, and pass into the circulation of the human body, becoming fluids and flesh of the same. Thus humors are introduced into the system. And if the person already has impure blood, it is greatly aggravated by eating of the flesh of these animals.— *T., V. II, p. 64.*

473. The very animals whose flesh you eat are frequently so diseased that, if left alone, they would die of themselves; but while the breath of life is in them, they are killed and brought to market. You take directly into your system humors and poisons of the worst kind, and yet you realize it not.— *T., V. II, p. 405.*

474. There are but few animals that are free from disease. Many have been made to suffer greatly for the want of light, pure air, and wholesome food. When they are fattened, they are often confined in close stables, and are not permitted to exercise, and to enjoy free circulation of air. Many poor animals are left to breathe the poison of filth which is left in barns and stables. Their lungs will not long remain healthy while inhaling such impurities. Disease is conveyed to the liver, and the entire system of the animal is diseased. They are killed,

and prepared for the market, and people eat freely of this poisonous animal food. Much disease is caused in this manner. But the people cannot be made to believe that it is the meat they have eaten which has poisoned their blood, and caused their sufferings. Many die of disease caused wholly by meat eating, yet the world does not seem to be the wiser. . . . It may be doing its work surely upon the system, and yet the person for the time being realize nothing of it.— *H. to L.*, *Chap. 1, p. 59*.

475. Animals are frequently killed that have been driven quite a distance to the slaughter. Their blood has become heated. They are of full flesh, and have been deprived of healthy exercise, and when they have to travel far, they become exhausted, and in that condition are killed for market. Their blood is highly inflamed, and those who eat of their meat, eat poison. Some are not immediately affected, while others are attacked with severe pain, and die from fever, cholera, or some unknown disease. . . . Some animals that are brought to the slaughter seem to realize what is to take place, and they become furious, and literally mad. They are killed while in this state, and their flesh is prepared for market. Their meat is poison, and has produced, in those who have eaten it, cramps, convulsions, apoplexy, and sudden death.— *H. to L.*, *Chap. 1, pp. 59, 60*.

476. Swine have been prepared for market even while the plague was upon them, and their poisonous flesh has spread contagious diseases, and great mortality has followed.— *H. to L.*, *Chap. 1, p. 60*.

477. Meat eating is doing its work, for the meat is diseased.— *U. T., Aug. 30, 1896.*

478. The flesh which they ate was diseased, and their entire system was becoming gross and corrupted.— *U. T., Aug. 30, 1897.*

479. Death was caused by the abundant eating of meat which at the last was tainted.— *U. T., Nov. 5, 1896.*

480. Pulmonary diseases, cancers, and tumors are startlingly common among animals. It is true that the inspectors reject many cattle that are diseased, but many are passed on to the market that ought to have been refused. . . . Thus unwholesome flesh has gone on the market for human consumption. In many localities even fish is unwholesome, and ought not to be used. This is especially so where the fish come in contact with the sewerage of large cities. . . . The fish that partake of the filthy sewerage of the drains may pass into waters far distant from the sewerage, and be caught in localities where the water is pure and fresh; but because of the unwholesome drainage in which they have been feeding, they are not safe to eat.— *U. T., Jan. 19, 1895.*

481. The fact that meat is largely diseased should lead us to make strenuous efforts to discontinue its use entirely. . . . It will be hard for some to do this, as hard as for the rum drinker to forsake his dram; but they will be better for the change.— *U. T., Nov. 9, 1896.*

CHAPTER XX.

STIMULANTS.

482. The use of unnatural stimulants is destructive to health, and has a benumbing influence upon the brain, making it impossible to appreciate eternal things.— *T., V. I, p. 549.*

483. Never be betrayed into indulging in the use of stimulants ; for this will result not only in reaction and loss of physical strength, but in a benumbed intellect.— *T., V. IV, p. 214.*

484. It is these hurtful stimulants that are surely undermining the constitution and preparing the system for acute diseases, by impairing nature's fine machinery, and battering down her fortifications erected against disease and premature decay.— *T., V. I, p. 549.*

485. Because these stimulants produce for the time being such agreeable results, many conclude that they really need them, and continue their use. But there is always a reaction. The nervous system, having been unduly excited, borrowed power for present use from its future resources of strength. All this temporary invigoration of the system is followed by depression. In proportion as these stimulants temporarily invigorate the system, will be the letting down of the power of the excited organs after the stimulus has lost its force.— *T., V. III, p. 487.*

486. Excitement will be followed by repression.—
R. and H., 1883, No. 19.

487. Tea has an influence to excite the nerves, **Tea and**
and coffee benumbs the brain; both are highly in- **Coffee.**
jurious.— *T., V. IV, p. 365.*

488. Tea, coffee, and flesh meats produce an immediate effect. Under the influence of these poisons the nervous system is excited, and in some
cases, for the time being, the intellect seems to be
invigorated, and the imagination to be more vivid.
— *T., V. III, p. 487.*

489. To a certain extent, tea produces intoxication. It enters into the circulation, and gradually
impairs the energy of body and mind. It stimulates,
excites, and quickens the motion of the living machinery, forcing it to unnatural action, and thus
gives the tea drinker the impression that it is doing
him great service, imparting to him strength. This
is a mistake. Tea draws upon the strength of the
nerves, and leaves them greatly weakened. When its
influence is gone and the increased action caused by
its use is abated, then what is the result?— Languor
and debility corresponding to the artificial vivacity
the tea imparted. When the system is already overtaxed and needs rest, the use of tea spurs up nature
by stimulation to perform unwonted, unnatural action, and thereby lessens her power to perform, and
her ability to endure; and her powers give out long
before Heaven designed they should. Tea is poisonous to the system. Christians should let it alone.
. . . The second effect of tea drinking is headache,
wakefulness, palpitation of the heart, indigestion,

trembling of the nerves, and many other evils.— *T.*, *V. II, pp. 64, 65.*

490. The influence of coffee is in a degree the same as tea, but the effect upon the system is still worse. Its influence is exciting, and just in the degree that it elevates above par, it will exhaust and bring prostration below par. Tea and coffee drinkers carry the marks upon their faces. The skin becomes sallow, and assumes a lifeless appearance. The glow of health is not seen upon the countenance.

Tea and coffee do not nourish the system. The relief obtained from them is sudden, before the stomach has had time to digest them. This shows that what the users of these stimulants call strength .is only received by exciting the nerves of the stomach, which convey the irritation to the brain, and this in turn is aroused to impart increased action to the heart, and short-lived energy to the entire system. All this is false strength, that we are the worse for having. They do not give a particle of natural strength.— *T., V. II, p. 65.*

491. The stimulating diet and drink of this day are not conducive to the best state of health. Tea, coffee, and tobacco are all stimulating, and contain poisons. They are not only unnecessary, but harmful, and should be discarded if we would add to knowledge temperance.—*R. and H., 1888, No. 8.*

492. Light has been given showing the injurious effects of tea, coffee, and flesh meats ; but this light has been disregarded, even by some who profess to believe the Testimonies. They even feel that to

deny themselves of these health-destroying indulgences would be a restriction of their liberty. If deprived for a time of their meat, tea, and coffee, they feel the loss, because of former indulgences, and are always pleading to be allowed to use them in some form. Enlighten their minds by means of talks and lectures, in regard to the effects of tea, coffee, and flesh meats, and thus lead them to a voluntary correction of their habits.— *U. T.*

493. He calls upon them to sacrifice their idols. They should lay aside such stimulants as tobacco, tea, and coffee.— *T., V. I, p. 224.*

494. The highly seasoned flesh meats and tea and coffee, which some mothers encourage their children to use, prepare the way for them to crave stronger stimulants, as tobacco.— *T., V. III, p. 488.*

495. The use of tobacco encourages the appetite **Tobacco.** for liquor; and the use of tobacco and liquor invariably lessens nerve power.— *T., V. III, p. 488.*

496. By the use of alcoholic drinks and narcotics and the flesh of diseased animals, man has distorted and crippled the Lord's divine arrangements. Nature does her best to expel the poisonous drug tobacco, but frequently she is overborne, gives up her struggle, and life is sacrificed in the conflict.— *U. T., Jan. 11, 1897.*

497. Tobacco, in whatever form it is used, tells upon the constitution. It is a slow poison. It affects the brain and benumbs the sensibilities so that the mind cannot discern spiritual things, especially those truths which would have a tendency to correct this filthy indulgence. Those who use

tobacco in any form are not clear before God.   In such a filthy practise it is impossible for them to glorify God in their bodies and spirits, which are his.   And while they are using slow and sure poisons, which are ruining their health and debasing the faculties of the mind, God cannot approbate them.   He may be merciful to them while they indulge in this pernicious habit in ignorance of the injury it is doing them; but when the matter is set before them in its true light, then they are guilty before God if they continue to indulge this gross appetite.— *F. of F., p. 126.*

498. Tobacco is a poison of the most deceitful and malignant kind, having an exciting, then a paralyzing, influence upon the nerves of the body. It is all the more dangerous because its effects upon the system are so slow, and at first scarcely perceivable.— *F. of F., p. 128.*

499. Tobacco is a slow, insidious poison, and its effects are more difficult to cleanse from the system than those of liquor.— *T., V. III, p. 569.*

500. Tobacco using is a habit which frequently affects the nervous system in a more powerful manner than does the use of alcohol.   It binds the victim in stronger bands of slavery than does the intoxicating cup; the habit is more difficult to overcome.   Body and mind are, in many cases, more thoroughly intoxicated with the use of tobacco than with spirituous liquors; for it is a more subtle poison.— *T., V. III, p. 562.*

501. It is unpleasant, if not dangerous, to remain in a railroad car or in a crowded room that is not

thoroughly ventilated, where the atmosphere is impregnated with the properties of liquor and tobacco. The occupants give evidence by the breath and emanations from the body that the system is filled with the poison of liquor and tobacco.— *T., V. III, p. 562.*

502. Many infants are poisoned beyond remedy by sleeping in beds with their tobacco-using fathers. By inhaling the poisonous tobacco effluvium, which is thrown from the lungs and pores of the skin, the system of the infant is filled with poison. While it acts upon some infants as a slow poison, and affects the brain, heart, liver, and lungs, and they waste away and fade gradually ; upon others it has a more direct influence, causing spasms, paralysis, and sudden death. The bereaved parents mourn the loss of their loved ones, and wonder at the mysterious providence of God, which has so cruelly afflicted them, when Providence designed not the death of these infants. They died martyrs to the filthy lust for tobacco. Every exhalation of the lungs of the tobacco slave poisons the air about him.— *H. R.*

503. Tobacco and liquor stupefy and defile the user. But the evil does not stop here. He transmits irritable tempers, polluted blood, enfeebled intellects, and weak morals to his children, and renders himself accountable for all the evil results that his wrong and dissipated course of life brings upon his family and the community.— *T., V. IV, p. 30.*

504. The tables of our American people are generally prepared in a manner to make drunkards. . . .   **Alcohol.**

By the use of tea and coffee an appetite is formed for tobacco, and this encourages the appetite for liquors. . . . Youth in general are governed by impulse and are slaves to appetite. In the glutton, the tobacco devotee, the wine-bibber, and the inebriate, we see the evil results of defective education.— *T., V. III, p. 563.*

505. The only safe course is to touch not, taste not, handle not, tea, coffee, wines, tobacco, opium, and alcoholic drinks.— *T., V. III, p. 488.*

506. If men would become temperate in all things, if they would touch not, taste not, handle not, spirituous liquors and narcotics, reason would hold the reins of government in her hands, and control the animal appetites and passions.— *T., V. III, p. 561.*

507. Persons may become just as really intoxicated on wine and cider as on stronger drinks, and the worst kind of inebriation is produced by these so-called milder drinks. The passions are more perverse; the transformation of character is greater, more determined and obstinate. A few quarts of cider or sweet wine may awaken a taste for strong drinks, and many who have become confirmed drunkards have thus laid the foundation of the drinking habit. . . . Moderate drinking is the school in which men are receiving an education for the drunkard's career. The taste for stimulants is cultivated; the nervous system is disordered; Satan keeps the mind in a fever of unrest; and the poor victim, imagining himself perfectly secure, goes on and on, until every barrier is broken down, every principle sacrificed.— *R. and H., 1884, No. 13.*

508. The Bible nowhere teaches the use of intoxicating wine, either as a beverage or as a symbol of the blood of Christ. We appeal to the natural reason whether the blood of Christ is better represented by the pure juice of the grape in its natural state, or after it has been converted into a fermented and intoxicating wine. . . . We urge that the latter should never be placed upon the Lord's table. . . . We protest that Christ never made intoxicating wine; such an act would have been contrary to all the teachings and examples of his life. . . . The wine which Christ manufactured from water by a miracle of his power was the pure juice of the grape.— *H. R.*

509. The use of tobacco and liquor invariably lessens nerve power.—*T., V. III, p. 489.*

Effects of the Use of Alcoholic Drinks.

510. A tendency to disease of various kinds, as dropsy, liver complaint, trembling nerves, and the determination of the blood to the head, results from the habitual use of sour cider. By its use many bring upon themselves permanent disease. Some die of consumption or fall under the power of apoplexy from this cause alone. Some suffer from dyspepsia. Every vital function refuses to act, and the physician tells them they have liver complaint, when if they would break in the head of the cider barrel, and never give way to the temptation to replace it, their abused life forces would recover their vigor.—*R. and H., 1884, No. 13.*

511. A single glass of wine may open the door of temptation which will lead to habits of drunkenness. —*T., V. IV, p. 578.*

512. When the appetite for spirituous liquor is indulged, the man voluntarily places to his lips the draught which debases below the level of the brute him who was made in the image of God. Reason is paralyzed, the intellect is benumbed, the animal passions are excited, and then follow crimes of the most debasing character.— *T., V. III, p. 561.*

513. The law authorizes the sale of liquor, and then has to build prisons for the victims ; for nine tenths of those who are taken to prison are those who have learned to drink.— *R. and H., 1894, No. 19.*

514. How many frightful accidents occur through the influence of drink. . . . What is the portion of this terrible intoxicant that any man can take, and be safe with the lives of human beings ? He can be safe only as he abstains from drink. No intoxicant should pass his lips ; then if a disaster comes, men in responsible positions can do their best, and meet their record with satisfaction, whatever may be the issue.— *R. and H., 1894, No. 22.*

515. Liquor-drinking men may be seen everywhere. Their intellect is enfeebled, their moral powers are weakened, their sensibilities are benumbed, and the claims of God and heaven are not realized, eternal things are not appreciated. The Bible declares that no drunkard shall inherit the kingdom of God. . . . Intemperance of any kind is the worst kind of selfishness.— *T., V. IV, pp. 30, 31.*

Cure for the Liquor Habit   516. What cure would you advise for a person who thus indulges a habit that is rebuked even by

the beasts of the field? The word of God has de-
nounced it: no drunkard shall enter the kingdom
of God. What would you recommend to cure such
an appetite? You would not say, "You may use
strong drink moderately. Continue within bounds,
but never indulge to excess." You would rather
say, "There is no such thing as helping you unless
you co-operate fully with my efforts, and sign the
pledge of total abstinence. You have by indulgence
made your habit second nature, and it cannot be
controlled unless the moral power shall be aroused,
and you look unto Jesus, trusting in the grace he
shall give to overcome this unnatural craving." You
would say, "You have lost your self-control. Your
self-indulgence is not only a moral sin, but it has
become a physical disease. You are not your own;
you are God's property. He has purchased you
with an infinite price, and every faculty is to be
employed in his service. Keep your body in a
healthy condition to do his will; keep your intellect
clear and active to think candidly and critically, and
to control all your powers." — *U. T., Oct. 12, 1896.*

517. The taste created for the disgusting, filthy
poison, tobacco, leads to the desire for stronger
stimulants, as liquor, which is taken on one plea or
another, for some imaginary infirmity, or to prevent
some possible disease. — *T., V. IV., p. 30.* {Alcohol in Disease.}

518. By advising friends and neighbors to take
brandy for the sake of their health, they are in
danger of becoming agents for the destruction of
their friends. . . . Physicians are responsible for
making many drunkards. Knowing what drink will

do for its lovers, they have taken upon themselves the responsibility of prescribing it for their patients. Did they reason from cause to effect, they would know that stimulants would have the same effect on each individual organ of the body that they have on the whole man. What excuse can doctors render for the influence they have exerted in making fathers and mothers drunkards? — *R. and H., 1894, No. 2.*

519. Go with me to yonder sick-room. There lies a husband and father, a man who is a blessing to society and to the cause of God. He has been suddenly stricken down by disease. The fire of fever seems consuming him. He longs for pure water to moisten the parched lips, to quench the raging thirst, and cool the fevered brow. But no; the doctor has forbidden water. The stimulus of strong drink is given, which adds fuel to the fire. . . . For a time nature wrestles for her rights, but at last, overcome, she gives up the contest, and death sets the sufferer free.— *T., No. 31, p. 191.*

520. Those who do not control their appetites in eating are guilty of intemperance. . . . With many, their first error is in making a god of their appetite, subsisting mostly on highly seasoned animal food, which produces a feverish state of the system, especially if pork is used freely. The blood becomes impure. The circulation is not equalized. Chills and fever follow. The appetite fails. They think something must be done, and perhaps send for ale, which stimulates for the time, but as soon as the influence of the ale is gone, they sink as much lower, and a continual use of the ale keeps them stimulated

and overexcited. They think that the ale was of so much benefit to them that they must continue its use. After a while it loses its influence; then they use a stronger beverage, until they give themselves up to every excess, and man formed in the image of his Maker degrades himself lower than the beasts. It required time to benumb the sensibilities of the mind. It was done gradually, but surely.— *F. of F.*, *p. 126.*

CHAPTER XXI.

DRESS.

General
Statements. 521. Our words, our actions, and our dress are daily, living preachers, gathering with Christ or scattering abroad. This is no trivial matter.— *T.*, *V. IV, p. 641.*

522. Turn away from the fashion plates, and study the human organism.— *C. T., p. 91.*

523. Christians should not take pains to make themselves a gazing-stock by dressing differently from the world. But if, when following out their convictions of duty in respect to dressing modestly and healthfully, they find themselves out of fashion, they should not change their dress in order to be like the world ; but they should manifest a noble independence and moral courage to be right, if all the world differ from them. If the world introduces a modest, convenient, and healthful mode of dress, which is in accordance with the Bible, it will not change our relation to God or to the world to adopt such a style of dress. Christians should follow Christ and make their dress conform to God's word. They should shun extremes.—*T., V. I, p. 458.*

524. In dress we should seek that which is simple, comfortable, convenient, and appropriate.—*R. and H., 1886, No. 24.*

525. A plain, direct testimony is now needed, as given in the word of God, in regard to plainness of dress. This should be our burden. But it is too late now to become enthusiastic in making a test of this matter. There were some things which made the reform dress, which was once advocated, a decided blessing. With it the ridiculous hoops, which were then the fashion, could not be worn. The long dress skirts trailing on the ground and sweeping up the filth of the streets could not be patronized. But a more sensible style of dress has been adopted, which does not embrace these objectionable features. The fashionable part may be discarded, and should be by all who read the word of God. The dress of our people should be made most simple. The skirt and sack I have mentioned may be used, not that just that pattern and nothing else should be established, but a simple style as was represented in that dress. Some have supposed that the very pattern given was the pattern that all should adopt; this is not so, but something as simple as this would be the best we could adopt under the circumstances. No one precise style has been given me as an exact rule to guide all in their dress. Let our sisters dress plainly, as many do, in having the dress of good material, durable, modest, appropriate for the age ; and let not the dress question fill the mind.— *U. T., July 4, 1897.*

Mental and Moral Influence of Dress.

526. The sum and substance of true religion is to own and continually acknowledge by words, by

dress, by deportment, our relationship to God.—
T., V. IV, p. 582.

527. Perhaps no question has ever come up among
us which has caused such development of character
as has the dress reform.— *T., V. IV, p. 636.*

528. Simplicity of dress will make a sensible woman
appear to the best advantage.   We judge of a person's
character by the style of dress worn.   Gaudy ap-
parel displays vanity and weakness.   A modest,
godly woman will dress modestly.   A refined taste,
a cultivated mind, will be revealed in the choice of
simple and appropriate attire.— *T., V. IV, p. 643.*

529. We would not by any means encourage carelessness in dress.   Let the attire be appropriate and
becoming.   Though only a ten-cent calico, it should
be kept neat and clean.—*T., V. IV, p. 642.*

530. Taste should be manifested as to colors.
Uniformity in this respect is desirable so far as convenient.   Complexion, however, may be taken into
account.   Modest colors should be sought for.
When figured material is used, figures that are large
and fiery, showing vanity and shallow pride in those
who choose them, should be avoided.   And a fan-
tastic taste in putting on different colors is bad.—
H. R.

531. Let the wearing of useless trimmings and
adornments be discarded.   Extravagance should
never be indulged in to gratify pride.   Our dress
may be of good quality, made up with plainness and
simplicity, for durability rather than for display.—
R. and H., 1878, No. 2.

532. There is no need to make the dress question the main point of your religion. There is something richer to speak of. Talk of Christ; and when the heart is converted, everything that is out of harmony with the word of God will drop off.— *S. of T., 1889, No. 25.*

533. There is no use in telling you that you must not wear this or that, for if the love of these vain things is in your heart, your laying off your adornments will only be like cutting the foliage off a tree.— *R. and H., 1892, No. 19.*

534. Obedience to fashion is pervading our Seventh-day Adventist churches, and is doing more than any other power to separate our people from God.— *T., V. IV, p. 647.*

535. As soon as any have a desire to imitate the fashions of the world that they do not immediately subdue, just so soon God ceases to acknowledge them as his children.— *T., V. I, p. 137.*

536. Those who have had the light upon the subjects of eating and dressing with simplicity, in obedience to physical and moral laws, and who turn from the light which points out their duty, will shun duty in other things. If they blunt their consciences to avoid the cross which they will have to take up to be in harmony with natural law, they will, in order to shun reproach, violate the ten command-ments.— *T., V. III, p. 51.*

Influence of Dress upon the Body.

537. Physical loveliness consists in symmetry — the harmonious proportion of parts.— *C. T., p. 94.*

Tight Clothing.

538. Dress reform . . . includes every article of dress upon the person. It lifts the weights from the hips by suspending the skirts from the shoulders. It removes the tight corsets, which compress the lungs, the stomach, and other internal organs, and induce curvature of the spine and an almost countless train of diseases. Dress reform proper provides for the protection and development of every part of the body.— *T., V. IV, p. 635.*

539. Woman's dress should be arranged so loosely upon the person, about the waist, that she can breathe without the least obstruction. Her arms should be left perfectly free, that she may raise them above her head with ease. . . . The compression of the waist by tight lacing prevents the waste matter from being thrown off through its natural channels. The most important of these is the lungs. . . . If the lungs are cramped, they cannot develop; but their capacity will be diminished, making it impossible to take a sufficient inspiration of air. . . . The compression of the waist weakens the muscles of the respiratory organs. It hinders the process of digestion. The heart, liver, lungs, spleen, and stomach are crowded into a small compass, not allowing room for the healthful action of these organs.— *H. R.; see also, C. T., p. 88.*

540. The dress should fit easily, obstructing neither the circulation of the blood, nor a free, full, natural respiration.— *C. T., p. 89.*

541. Our Creator made no mistake in fashioning the human body. He gave appropriate space for the free action of every organ, and formed us in

such a way that every muscle could come into play without trespassing upon the function of any other muscle.— *Y. I., Sept. 14, 1893.*

542. Lacing causes displacements, and this form of disease is increasing with each successive generation. — *H. R.*

543. Many have become lifelong invalids through their compliance with the demands of fashion. Displacements and deformities, cancers and other terrible diseases, are among the evils resulting from fashionable dress.— *T., V. IV, p. 635.*

544. Half the diseases of women are caused by unhealthful dress.—*H. R.*

545. The hips are not formed to bear heavy **Heavy** weights. The heavy skirts worn by women, their **Skirts** weight dragging down upon the hips, have been the cause of various diseases which are not easily cured, because the sufferers seem to be ignorant of the cause which has produced them, and they continue to violate the laws of their being by girding the waist and wearing heavy skirts, until they are made lifelong invalids.— *H. to L., Chap. 6, p. 64.*

546. This heavy weight pressing upon the bowels, drags them downward, and causes weakness of the stomach, and a feeling of lassitude, which leads the sufferer to incline forward. This tends further to cramp the lungs, and prevents their proper action. The blood becomes impure, the pores of the skin fail in their office, sallowness and disease result, and beauty and health are gone. . . . Every woman who values health should avoid hanging any weight upon the hips.— *C. T., p. 89.*

547. The most of us wear clothing enough, but many fail to give every part of the body its due proportion. . . . If any part of the body should be favored with extra coverings, it should be the limbs and feet, which are at a distance from the great wheel of life, which sends the blood through the system. The limbs should ever be clothed with a warm covering to protect them from a chill current of air. . . . If the feet are clothed with good-sized, thick-soled, warm boots or shoes, for comfort rather than for fashion, the blood will be induced to circulate freely in the limbs and feet, as well as other portions of the body. . . . If we give the lungs and feet ample room to do the work God designed they should, we shall be rewarded with better health and a clearer conscience.—*H. R.*

548. There is but one woman in a thousand who clothes her limbs as she should. . . . Women should clothe their limbs as thoroughly as do men. —*H. to L., Chap. 6, p. 64.*

549. The portions of the body close to the life springs, need less covering than the limbs which are remote from the vital organs. If the limbs and feet could have the extra coverings usually put upon the shoulders, lungs, and heart, and healthy circulation be induced to the extremities, the vital organs would act their part healthfully, with only their share of clothing.—*H. to L., Chap. 5, p. 73.*

550. The extremities are chilled, and the heart has thrown upon it double labor, to force the blood into these chilled extremities; and when the blood has performed its circuit through the body, and re-

turned to the heart, it is not the same vigorous, warm current which left it. It has been chilled in its passage through the limbs. The heart, weakened by too great labor and poor circulation of poor blood, is then compelled to still greater exertion, to throw the blood to the extremities which are never as healthfully warm as other parts of the body. The heart fails in its efforts, and the limbs become habitually cold ; and the blood, which is chilled away from the extremities, is thrown back upon the lungs and brain, and inflammation and congestion of the lungs or the brain is the result.— *H. to L.*, *Chap. 5*, *p. 72.*

551. It is impossible for women to have, habitually, chilled limbs and cold feet, without some of the internal organs' being congested. . . . The many extra coverings over the chest and back and lower part of the body, induce the blood to these parts, and the animal heat, thus retained, weakens and debilitates the delicate organs, and congestion and inflammation result.— *H. R.*

552. When the extremities, which are remote from the vital organs, are not properly clad, the blood is driven to the head, causing headache or nosebleed; or there is a sense of fulness about the chest producing cough or palpitation of the heart, on account of too much blood in that locality; or the stomach has too much blood, causing indigestion.— *T.*, *V. II, p. 531.*

553. The length of the fashionable dress is objectionable for several reasons : — **Length of Dress.**

1. It is extravagant and unnecessary to have a dress of such length that it will sweep the sidewalk and street.

2. A dress thus long gathers dew from the grass and mud from the streets, and is therefore uncleanly.

3. In its bedraggled condition it comes in contact with the sensitive ankles, which are not sufficiently protected, quickly chilling them, and thus endangering health and life. This is one of the greatest causes of catarrh and scrofulous swellings.

4. The unnecessary length is an additional weight upon the hips and bowels.

5. It hinders the walking, and is also often in other people's way.— *T., V. I, p. 459.*

If women would wear their dresses so as to clear the filth of the street an inch or two, their dresses would be modest, and they could be kept clean much more easily, and would wear longer.— *Ibid., p. 458.*

Too Much Clothing. 554. You have worn too great an amount of clothing, and have debilitated the skin by so doing. You have not given your body a chance to breathe. The pores of the skin, or little mouths through which the body breathes, have become closed, and the system has been filled with impurities.— *T., V. III, p. 74.*

555. I advise invalid sisters who have accustomed themselves to too great an amount of clothing, to lay it off gradually.— *T., V. II, p. 533.*

556. Disease of every type is brought upon the body through the unhealthful, fashionable style of dress ; and the fact should be made prominent that a reform must take place before treatment will effect a cure.— *T., V. IV, p. 582.*

CHAPTER XXII.

EXERCISE.

557. The human body may be compared to nicely **General Statements.** adjusted machinery, which needs care to keep it in running order. One part should not be subjected to constant wear and pressure, while another part is rusting from inaction. While the mind is taxed, the muscles also should have their proportion of exercise. Every young person should learn how many hours may be spent in study, and how much time should be given to physical exercise.— *S. of T., 1886, No. 33.*

558. There is quite a difference between weariness and exhaustion.— *S. A., p. 64.*

559. The compression of the waist will not allow free action of the muscles.— *H. R.*

560. Another precious blessing is proper exercise. — *T., V. II, p. 528.*

561. They should go out and exercise every day, . . . make it their object to do some good, working to the end of benefiting others.— *T., V. II, p. 531.*

Varieties of Exercise.

562. The exercise of one muscle, while others are **Gymnastics.** left with nothing to do, will not strengthen the inactive ones, any more than the continual exercise of one of the organs of the mind will develop and

strengthen the organs not brought into use.   Each faculty of the mind and each muscle has its distinctive office, and all require to be exercised in order to become properly developed and retain healthful vigor.   Each organ and muscle has its work to do in the living organism.   Every wheel in the machinery must be a living, active, working wheel.   Nature's fine and wonderful works need to be kept in active motion in order to accomplish the object for which they were designed.   Each faculty has a bearing upon the others, and all need to be exercised in order to be properly developed.   If one muscle of the body is exercised more than another, the one used will become much the larger, and will destroy the harmony and beauty of the development of the system.   A variety of exercise will call into use all the muscles of the body.— *T., V. III, pp. 77, 78.*

563. It is not good policy to give up the use of certain muscles because pain is felt when they are exercised.   The pain is frequently caused by the effort of nature to give life and vigor to those parts that have become partially lifeless through inaction.   The motion of these long disused muscles will cause pain, because nature is awakening them to life.— *T., V. III, p. 78.*

564. Exercise, to be of decided advantage to you, should be systematized, and brought to bear upon the debilitated organs that they may become strengthened by use.— *T., V. III, p. 76.*

Useful Labor.   565. When useful labor is combined with study, there is no need of gymnastic exercises; and much more benefit is derived from work performed in the open air than from indoor exercise. The farmer and the mechanic each have physical exercise; yet the farmer is much the healthier of the two, for nothing short of the invigorating air and sunshine will fully meet the wants of the system. The former finds in his labor all the movements that were ever practised in the gymnasium. And his movement room is the open fields; the canopy of heaven is its roof, the solid earth is its floor.— *S. of T., 1886, No. 33.*

566. Brethren, when you take time to cultivate your gardens, thus gaining the exercise needed to keep the system in good working order, you are just as much doing the work of God as in holding meetings.— *G. W., p. 174.*

567. If work is performed without the heart's being in it, it is simply drudgery, and the benefit which should result from the exercise is not gained.— *H. R.*

568. The movement cure is a great advantage to a class of patients who are too feeble to exercise. But for all who are sick to rely upon it, making it their dependence, while they neglect to exercise their muscles themselves, is a great mistake.— *T., V. III, p. 76.* **Passive Exercise**

569. Many who depend on the movement cure could accomplish more for themselves by muscular exercise than the movements can do for them.— *T., V. III, p. 78.*

570. There is no exercise that can take the place of walking. By it the circulation of the blood is greatly improved. . . . Walking, in all cases where it is possible, is the best remedy for diseased bodies, **Walking**

because in this exercise all of the organs of the body are brought into use.— *T.*, *V. III, p. 78.*

571. When the weather will permit, all who can possibly do so ought to walk in the open air every day, summer and winter. . . . A walk, even in winter, would be more beneficial to the health than all the medicine the doctors may prescribe. For those who can walk, walking is preferable to riding. The muscles and veins are enabled better to perform their work. There will be increased vitality, which is so necessary to health. The lungs will have needful action; for it is impossible to go out in the bracing air of a winter's morning without inflating the lungs.— *T.*, *V. II, p. 529.*

572. There is no exercise that will prove as beneficial to every part of the body as walking. Active walking in the open air will do more for women, to preserve them in health if they are well, than any other means. Walking is also one of the most efficient remedies for the recovery of health of the invalid. The hands and arms are exercised as well as the limbs.— *H. R.*

When to Exercise.

573. Exercise will aid the work of digestion. To walk out after a meal, hold the head erect, put back the shoulders, and exercise moderately, will be a great benefit. The mind will be diverted from self to the beauties of nature. The less the attention is called to the stomach after a meal, the better.— *T.*, *V. II, p. 530.*

574. Morning exercise, in walking in the free, invigorating air of heaven, or cultivating flowers, small fruits, and vegetables, is necessary to a health-

ful circulation of the blood. It is the surest safe-guard against colds, coughs, congestions of the brain and lungs, inflammation of the liver, the kidneys, and the lungs, and a hundred other diseases.— *H. R.*

575. A large class of women are content to hover over the stove, breathing impure air for one half or three fourths of the time, until the brain is heated and half benumbed. They should go out and exercise every day, even though some things indoors have to be neglected. They need the cool air to quiet distracted brains.— *T., V. II, p. 531.*

576. Neither study nor violent exercise should be engaged in immediately after a full meal; this would be a violation of the laws of the system. Immediately after eating there is a strong draught upon the nervous energy. The brain force is called into active exercise to assist the stomach; therefore, when mind or body is taxed heavily after eating, the process of digestion is hindered. The vitality of the system, which is needed to carry on the work in one direction, is called away and set to work in another.— *T., V. II, p. 413.*

577. God designed that the living machinery should be in daily activity; for in this activity or motion is its preserving power.— *H. R.*

Benefits Derived from Exercise.

578. By active exercise in the open air every day the liver, kidneys, and lungs also will be strengthened to perform their work.— *T., V. II, p. 533.*

579. If invalids who can would engage in light, useful labor in the open air a portion of each day, they would find physical exercise one of God's appointed agents for the benefit of man.— *H. R.*

580. If they worked intelligently, giving both mind and body a due share of exercise, ministers would not so readily succumb to disease.— *G. W.*, *p. 173.*

581. Healthy, active exercise is what you need. This will invigorate the mind.— *T., V. II, p. 413.*

582. There will be increased vitality, which is so necessary to health.— *T., V. II, p. 529.*

583. Not only will the organs of the body be strengthened by exercise, but the mind also will acquire strength and knowledge through the action of these organs.— *T., V. III, p. 77.*

584. The more we exercise, the better will be the circulation of the blood.— *T., V. II, p. 525.*

585. If physical exercise were combined with mental exertion, the blood would be quickened in its circulation, the action of the heart would be more perfect, impure matter would be thrown off, and new life and vigor would be experienced in every part of the body.— *T., V. III, p. 490.*

586. The proper use of their physical strength, as well as of the mental powers, will equalize the circulation of the blood, and keep every organ of the living machinery in running order.— *S. T. on E., p. 352.*

587. Judicious exercise will induce the blood to the surface, and thus relieve the internal organs. Brisk, yet not violent, exercise in the open air, with cheerfulness of spirits, will promote the circulation, giving a healthful glow to the skin, and sending the blood, vitalized by the pure air, to the extremities. —*T., V. II, p. 530.*

588. By judicious exercise they may expand the chest and strengthen the muscles. . . . By giving heed to proper instruction, by following health principles in regard to the expansion of the lungs and culture of the voice, our young men and women may become speakers that can be heard, and the exercise necessary to this accomplishment will prolong life.— *C. E.*, *p. 132.*

589. A farmer who is temperate in all his habits usually enjoys good health. His work is pleasant; and his vigorous exercise causes full, deep, and strong inspirations and exhalations, which expand the lungs and purify the blood, sending the warm current of life bounding through arteries and veins. . . . The student sits day after day in a close room, bending over his desk or table, his chest contracted, his lungs crowded. His brain is taxed to the utmost, while his body is inactive. He cannot take full, deep inspirations; his blood moves sluggishly; his feet are cold, his head hot. . . . Let them take regular exercise that will cause them to breathe deep and full, and they will soon feel that they have a new hold on life.— *S. of T.*, *1886,* *No. 33.*

590. The diseased stomach will find relief by exercise.— *T.*, *V. II*, *p. 530.*

591. Exercise is important to digestion, and to a healthy condition of body and mind.— *T.*, *V. II*, *p. 413.*

592. Digestion will be promoted by physical exercise.— *T.*, *V. II*, *p. 569.*

593. Useful employment would bring into exercise the enfeebled muscles, enliven the stagnant blood in the system, and arouse the torpid liver to perform its work. The circulation of the blood would be equalized, and the entire system invigorated to overcome bad conditions.— *H. R.*

Results of Lack of Exercise.

594. I frequently turn from the bedside of these self-made invalids, saying to myself, "Dying by inches, dying of indolence, a disease which no one but themselves can cure."— *H. R.*

595. Neglecting to exercise the entire body, or a portion of it, will bring on morbid conditions.— *T., V. III, p. 76.*

596. The bloom of health fades from their cheeks, and disease fastens upon them, because they are robbed of physical exercise, and their habits are perverted generally.— *T., V. III, p. 158.*

597. Continued inactivity is one of the greatest causes of debility of body and feebleness of mind.— *T., V. II, p. 524.*

598. Inaction of any of the organs of the body will be followed by decrease in size and strength of the muscles, and will cause the blood to flow sluggishly through the blood-vessels.— *T., V. III, p. 76.*

599. In what contrast to the habits of the active farmer are those of the student who neglects physical exercise. . . . His blood moves sluggishly; his feet are cold; his head hot. How can such a person have health ?— *S. of T., 1886, No. 33.*

600. The studied habit of shunning the air and avoiding exercise, closes the pores,— the little mouths through which the body breathes,— making it impos-

sible to throw off impurities through that channel. The burden of labor is thrown upon the liver, lungs, kidneys, etc., and these internal organs are compelled to do the work of the skin.— *T.*, *V. II, p. 524.*

601. The blood is not enabled to expel the impurities as it would if active circulation were induced by exercise.— *T.*, *V. II, p. 529.*

602. In some cases, want of exercise causes the muscles of the bowels to become enfeebled and shrunken, and these organs that have become enfeebled for want of use will be strengthened by exercise.— *T.*, *V. III, p. 78.*

603. Moderate exercise every day will impart strength to the muscles, which without exercise become flabby and enfeebled.— *T.*, *V. II, p. 533.*

604. If invalids would recover health, they should not discontinue physical exercise; for they will thus increase muscular weakness and general debility. Bind up the arm, and permit it to remain useless, even for a few weeks, then free it from its bondage, and you will discover that it is weaker than the one you had been using moderately during the same time. Inactivity produces the same effect upon the whole muscular system.— *T.*, *V. II, p. 529.*

CHAPTER XXIII.

MANUAL TRAINING.

605. If all our workers were so situated that they could spend a few hours each day in outdoor labor, and feel free to do this, it would be a blessing to them; they would be able to discharge more successfully the duties of their calling.— *G. W., p. 173.*

606. Manual occupation for the youth is essential. . . . The proper exercise of mind and body will develop and strengthen all the powers. Both mind and body will be preserved, and will be capable of doing a variety of work. Ministers and teachers need to learn in regard to these things, and they need to practise as well.— *Sp. Inst. on Ed. Work, p. 14.*

607. The people of this country have so little appreciation of the importance of industrious habits that the children are not educated to do real, earnest work. This must be a part of the education given to the youth. . . . We need schools to educate children and youth that they may be *masters* of labor, and not *slaves* of labor. Ignorance and idleness will not elevate one member of the human family. Ignorance will not lighten the lot of the hard toiler. Let the worker see what advantage he may gain in the humblest occupation, by using the ability God has given him as an endowment. Thus he can be-

come an educator, teaching others the art of doing work intelligently. . . . The Lord wants the physical strength; and you can reveal your love for him by the right use of your physical powers, doing the very work which needs to be done. . . . There is science in the humblest kind of work, and if all would thus regard it, they would see nobility in labor. . . . Let the educated ability be employed in devising improved methods of work. This is just what the Lord wants. There is honor in any class of work that is essential to be done. Let the law of God be made the standard of action, and it ennobles and sanctifies all labor. . . . We are not to be dwarfed in any kind of service for God. Whatever he has lent us is to be used intelligently for him. The man who exercises his faculties will surely strengthen them; but he must seek to do his best. There is need of intelligence and educated ability to devise the best methods in farming, in building, and in every other department, that the worker may not labor in vain.— *Sp. Inst. on Ed. Work, p. 5.*

608. Your means could not be used to better advantage than in providing a workshop furnished with tools for your boys, and equal facilities for your girls. They can be taught to love labor.— *H. R.*

609. Agriculture will open resources for self-support, and various other trades also could be learned. This real, earnest work calls for a strength of intellect as well as of muscle. Method and tact are required even to raise fruits and vegetables successfully. And habits of industry will be found an

important aid to the youth in resisting temptation. Here is opened a field to give vent to their pent-up energies, that, if not expended in useful employment, will be a continual source of trial to themselves and to their teachers. Many kinds of labor adapted to different persons may be devised. But the working of the land will be a special blessing to the worker. . . . This knowledge will not be a hindrance to the education essential for business or for usefulness in any line. To develop the capacity of the soil requires thought and intelligence.— *Sp. Inst. on Ed. Work, p. 15.*

610. Agriculture should be advanced by scientific knowledge.— *S. of T., 1896, No. 32.*

611. Students sent to school to prepare to become evangelists, ministers, and missionaries to foreign countries, have received the idea that amusements are essential to keep them in physical health, when the Lord has presented it before them that the better way is to embrace in their education manual labor in place of amusement. . . . The education to be obtained in felling trees, tilling the soil, as well as in literature, is the education our youth should seek to obtain. Farther on printing-presses should be connected with our schools. Tent making also should be taken hold of. Buildings should be erected, and masonry should be learned.

There are also many things which the lady students may engage in. There is cooking, dressmaking, and gardening to be done. Strawberries should be planted, and plants and flowers cultivated.

Bookbinding also and a variety of trades should

be taken up. Thus the student will be putting into exercise bone, brain, and muscle, and will also be gaining knowledge. The greatest curse of our schools is idleness. It leads to amusements merely to please and gratify self. The students have had a superabundance of this way of passing their time. They are not prepared to go forth from the school with an all-round education.

The proper cooking of food is a most essential requirement. Something must be prepared to take the place of meat, and so well prepared that meat will not be desired. Culture on all points of life will make the youth useful after they shall leave the school to go to foreign countries. They will not then have to depend upon the people to whom they go to cook and sew for them, or to build their habitations; and they will have much more influence if they show that they know how to do work by the best methods and to produce the best results. This will be appreciated where means are difficult to obtain. Missionaries can thus teach others how to labor. A much smaller fund will be required to sustain such missionaries, and wherever they may go, all that they have gained in this line will give them standing.

It is also essential to understand the philosophy of medical missionary work. Wherever the students may go, they need education in the science of how to treat the sick. This will give them a welcome in any place, because there is suffering of every kind in every part of the world. Education, true education, means much.— *U. T., Dec. 20, 1896.*

CHAPTER XXIV.

HYGIENE.

Hygiene of the Home and Premises.

612. Dwellings, if possible, should be built upon high and dry ground. If a house be built where water settles around it, remaining for a time and then drying away, a poisonous miasma arises, and fever and ague, sore throat, lung diseases, and fevers will be the result.—*H. to L., Chap. 4, p. 64.*

613. If every family realized the beneficial results of thorough cleanliness, they would make special efforts to remove every impurity from their persons and from their houses, and would extend their efforts to their premises. Many suffer decayed vegetable matter to remain about their premises. They are not awake to the influence of these things. There is constantly arising from the decayed substances an effluvium that is poisoning the air. By inhaling the impure air, the blood is poisoned, the lungs become affected, and the whole system is diseased.—*H. to L., Chap. 4, p. 60.*

614. Stubborn fevers and violent diseases have prevailed in neighborhoods and towns that had formerly been considered healthy, and some have died, while others have been left with broken constitutions to be crippled with disease for life. In many

instances their own yards contained the agent of destruction, which sent forth deadly poison into the atmosphere to be inhaled by the family and the neighborhood. The slackness and recklessness sometimes witnessed is beastly, and the ignorance of the results of such things upon health is astonishing. Such places should be purified, especially in summer, by lime or ashes, or by a daily burial with earth.— *H. to L., Chap. 4, p. 61.*

615. Shade-trees and shrubbery too close and dense around a house are unhealthful; for they prevent a free circulation of air, and prevent the rays of the sun from shining through sufficiently. In consequence of this a dampness gathers in the house. Especially in wet seasons the sleeping-rooms become damp, and those who sleep in the beds are troubled with rheumatism, neuralgia, and lung complaints, which generally end in consumption. Numerous shade-trees cast off many leaves, which, if not immediately removed, decay, and poison the atmosphere. A yard, beautiful with scattering trees, and some shrubbery at a proper distance from the house, has a happy, cheerful influence upon the family, and if well taken care of, will prove no injury to health.— *H. to L., Chap. 4, p. 64.*

616. Rooms that are not exposed to light and air become damp. Beds and bedding gather dampness, and the atmosphere in these rooms is poisonous, because it has not been purified by light and air. Various diseases have been brought on by sleeping in these fashionable, health-destroying apartments. . . . Sleeping-rooms especially should be well venti-

lated, and the atmosphere made healthful by light and air. Blinds should be left open several hours each day, the curtains put aside, and the room thoroughly aired; nothing should remain, even for a short time, which would destroy the purity of the atmosphere.—*H. to L., Chap. 4, p. 62.*

617. Sleeping apartments should be large and so arranged as to have a circulation of air through them day and night.—*H. to L., Chap. 4, p. 63.*

618. Rooms that are not freely ventilated daily, and bedding that has not been thoroughly dried and aired, are not fit for use. We feel confident that disease and great suffering are brought on by sleeping in rooms with closed and curtained windows, not admitting pure air and the rays of the sun. . . . The room may not have had an airing for months, nor the advantages of a fire for weeks, if at all. It is dangerous to health and life to sleep in these rooms until the outside air shall have circulated through them for several hours and the bedding shall have been dried by the fire. Unless this precaution is taken, the rooms and bedding will be damp. Every room in the house should be thoroughly ventilated every day, and in damp weather should be warmed by fires. . . . Every room in your dwelling should be daily thrown open to the healthful rays of the sun, and the purifying air should be invited in. This will be a preventive of disease. . . . If all would appreciate the sunshine, and expose every article of clothing to its drying, purifying rays, mildew and mold would be prevented. The confined air of unventilated rooms meets us with sickening odors of mildew and

mold, and the impurities exhaled by its inmates. . . . The emanations from damp, moldy rooms and clothing are poisonous to the system.—*H. R.*

Hygiene of the Person.

619. Strict habits of cleanliness should be observed. Many, while well, will not take the trouble to keep in a healthy condition. They neglect personal cleanliness, and are not careful to keep their clothing pure. Impurities are constantly and imperceptibly passing from the body, through the pores, and if the surface of the skin is not kept in a healthy condition, the system is burdened with impure matter. If the clothing worn is not often washed, and frequently aired, it becomes filthy with impurities which are thrown off from the body by sensible and insensible perspiration. And if the garments worn are not frequently cleansed from these impurities, the pores of the skin absorb again the waste matter thrown off. The impurities of the body, if not allowed to escape, are taken back into the blood, and forced upon the internal organs.—*H. to L., Chap. 4, p. 60.*

620. In regard to cleanliness, God requires no less of his people now than he did of ancient Israel. A neglect of cleanliness will induce disease.—*H. to L., Chap. 4, p. 61.*

621. The ten commandments spoken by Jehovah from Sinai cannot live in the hearts of persons of disorderly, filthy habits. If ancient Israel could not so much as listen to the proclamation of that holy law, unless they had obeyed the injunction of Jeho-

vah, and had cleansed their clothing, how can that sacred law be written upon the hearts of persons who are not cleanly in person, in clothing, or in their houses ? It is impossible. Their profession may be as high as heaven, yet it is not worth a straw. . . . All who meet upon the Sabbath to worship God should, if possible, have a neat, well-fitting, comely suit to wear in the house of worship. It is a dishonor to the Sabbath, and to God and his house, for those who profess that the Sabbath is the holy of the Lord, and honorable, to wear the same clothing upon the Sabbath that they have worn through the week while laboring upon their farms, when they can obtain other.— *H. to L., Chap. 6, p. 59.*

Hygiene for Children.

General
Statements.

622. Several instances have come under my notice where children are being murdered by inches by the mistaken kindness of parents.— *H. R.*

623. The calm, self-possessed course the mother pursues in the treatment of her child has very much to do in molding the mind of the infant. If it is nervous and easily agitated, the mother's careful, unhurried manner will have a soothing and correcting influence, and the health of the infant can be very much improved.— *H. to L., Chap. 2, p. 39.*

Diet.

624. It ever has appeared to me to be cold, heartless business for mothers who can nurse their children to turn them from the maternal breast to the bottle. But in case that is necessary, the greatest care must be exercised to have the milk from a healthy cow, and to have the bottle, as well as the

milk, perfectly sweet. This is frequently neglected, and as the result, the infant is made to suffer needlessly. Disturbances of the stomach and bowels are liable to occur, and the much-to-be-pitied infant becomes diseased, if it were healthy when born.— *H. R.*

625. Mothers sometimes depend upon a hireling. **Hired Nurses.** . . . A stranger performs the duties of the mother, and gives from her breast the food to sustain life. Nor is this all. She also imparts her temper and her temperament to the nursing child. The child's life is linked to hers. If the hireling is a coarse type of woman, passionate and unreasonable; if she is not careful in her morals, the nursling will be, in all probability, of the same or similar type. The same quality of blood coursing in the veins of the hireling nurse is in that of the child.— *H. R.*

626. Children are also fed too frequently, which **Frequent Feeding.** produces feverishness and suffering in various ways. The stomach should not be kept constantly at work, but should have its periods of rest. Without it children will be peevish and irritable and frequently sick.— *H. R.*

627. The first education that children should receive from the mother in infancy should be in regard to their physical health. They should be allowed only plain food, of that quality that would preserve to them the best condition of health, and that should be partaken of only at regular periods, not oftener than three times a day, and two meals would be better than three. If children are disciplined aright, they will soon learn they can re-

ceive nothing by crying and fretting. A judicious mother will act in training her children, not merely in regard to her own present comfort, but for their future good. And to this end she will teach her children the important lesson of controlling the appetite, and of self-denial, that they should eat, drink, and dress in reference to health.— *H. to L.*, *Chap. 2, p. 47.*

628. It is much easier to create an unnatural appetite than to correct and reform it after it has become second nature. . . . Meat given to children is not the best thing to insure success. . . . To educate your children to subsist upon a meat diet would be harmful to them. . . . Highly seasoned meats, followed by rich pastry, is wearing out the vital organs of the digestion of children. Had they been accustomed to plain, wholesome food, their appetites would not have craved unnatural luxuries and mixed preparations.— *U. T., Nov. 5, 1896.*

Fresh Air.   629. One great error of the mother in the treatment of her infant is, she deprives it very much of fresh air, that which it ought to have to make it strong. It is a practise of many mothers to cover their infant's head while sleeping, and this, too, in a warm room, which is seldom ventilated as it should be. This alone is sufficient to greatly enfeeble the action of the heart and lungs, thereby affecting the whole system. While care may be needful to protect the infant from a draught of air or from any sudden and too great change, especial care should be taken to have the child breathe a pure, invigorating atmosphere. No disagreeable odor should remain in the nursery or about the child; such things are more dangerous to the feeble infant than to grown persons.— *H. to L., Chap. 5, p. 66.*

630. But there is an evil greater than those already named. The infant is exposed to a vitiated air caused by many breaths, some of which are very offensive and injurious to the strong lungs of older people. The infant lungs suffer and become diseased by inhaling the atmosphere of a room poisoned by the tobacco user's tainted breath. Many infants are poisoned beyond remedy by sleeping in beds with their tobacco-using fathers. By inhaling the poisonous tobacco effluvium, which is thrown from the lungs and the pores of the skin, the system of the infant is filled with the poison. While it acts upon some as a slow poison, and affects the brain, heart, liver, and lungs, and they waste away and fade gradually, upon others it has a more direct influence, causing spasms, fits, paralysis, palsy, and sudden death.— *H. to L., Chap. 5, p. 68.*

631. The garments are made extravagantly long, **Dress of the Infant.** and in order to keep them up on the infant, its body is girded with tight bands, or waists, which hinder the free action of the heart and lungs. Infants are compelled to bear a needless weight because of the length of their garments, and thus clothed, they do not have free use of their muscles and limbs. Mothers have thought it necessary to compress the bodies of their infant children to keep them in shape, as if fearful that without tight bandages they would fall in pieces or become deformed. Do the animal creation become deformed because nature

is left to do her own work? Do the little lambs
become deformed because they are not girded about
with bands to give them shape? They are delicately
and beautifully formed.   Human infants are the
most perfect, and yet the most helpless, of all the
Creator's handiwork, and therefore their mothers
should be instructed in regard to physical laws, so
as to be capable of rearing them with physical,
mental, and moral health.   Mothers, nature has
given your infants forms which need no girts or
bands to perfect them.   God has supplied them
with bones and muscles sufficient for their support,
and to guard nature's fine machinery within, before
committing it to your care.   The dress of the infant
should be so arranged that its body will not be in
the least compressed after taking a full meal. . . .
Another great cause of mortality among infants and
youth, is the custom of leaving their arms and shoulders naked.   This fashion cannot be too severely
censured.   It has cost the lives of thousands.   The
air, bathing the arms and limbs and circulating
about the armpits, chills these sensitive portions of
the body so near the vitals, hinders the healthy
circulation of the blood, and induces disease,
especially of the lungs and brain.— *H. to L.*,
Chap. 5, pp. 67-69.

632. Mothers who dress their children in accordance with fashion, endanger their health and life.
Fashion leaves the limbs of children unclad, save
with one covering, or, at most, two.   If they are exposed to the chill autumn, spring, or winter weather,
their limbs are bathed in a current of cold air.   Over

the heart, where is the greatest amount of vitality,
there are from four to eight coverings. These unclad limbs and feet become habitually cold. While
traveling, it is customary to see little girls dressed
fashionably, but not healthfully The upper portions of the body are abundantly clothed with warm
cloaks, and over these are furs, while the limbs are
scarcely covered. . . . Christian mother, why not
clothe your daughter as comfortably and as properly
as you do your son? . . . His limbs are protected
by from three to five thicknesses; hers by only one.
Is she feebler? Then she needs the greater care.
Is she indoors more, and therefore less protected
against cold and storm? Then she needs double
care.—*H. R.*

633. Societies are formed in our cities for the
prevention of cruelty to dumb animals. It would be
well to go still further, and, inasmuch as accountable intelligences, capable of obtaining life eternal,
are of more value than the dumb beasts, there is
greater need of societies to prevent the cruelty of
mothers in dressing their darling little girls in a manner to sacrifice them at the shrine of cruel fashion.
—*H. R.*

634. There is a disposition with many parents to **Drugs.**
dose children perpetually with medicine. They always have a supply on hand, and when any slight
indisposition is manifested, caused by overeating or
exhaustion, the medicine is poured down their
throats, and if that does not satisfy them, they send
for the doctor. . . . The child is drugged to
death, and the parents console themselves that they

have done all they could for their children, and wonder why they must die when they did so much to
save them. . . . Upon the gravestones of such children should be written, "Died of Drug Medication."
— *H. R.*

Schools.   635. Many mothers feel that they have not time to
instruct their children, and in order to get them out
of the way, and get rid of their noise and trouble,
they send them to school. The schoolroom is a
hard place for children who have inherited enfeebled
constitutions. Schoolrooms generally have not been
constructed in reference to health, but in regard to
cheapness. The rooms have not been arranged so
they could be ventilated as they should be without
exposing the children to severe colds. The seats
have seldom been made so that the children can sit
with ease, and keep their little, growing frames in a
proper posture to insure healthy action of the lungs
and heart. Young children can grow into almost any
shape, and can, by habits of proper exercise and positions of the body, obtain healthy forms. It is destructive to the health and life of young children to
sit in the schoolroom, upon hard, ill-formed benches,
from three to five hours a day, inhaling the air made
impure by many breaths. The weak lungs become
affected, the brain, from which the nervous energy
of the whole system is derived, becomes enfeebled
by being called into active exercise before the
strength of the mental organs is sufficiently matured
to endure fatigue.

In the schoolroom the foundation has been too
surely laid for diseases of various kinds. But, more

especially, the most delicate of all organs, the brain, has often been permanently injured by too great exercise. This has often caused inflammation, then dropsy of the head, and convulsions with their dreaded results. . . . Of those children who have apparently had sufficient force of constitution to survive this treatment, there are very many who carry the effects of it through life. The nervous energy of the brain becomes so weakened that after they have come to maturity it is impossible for them to endure much mental exercise. The force of some of the delicate organs of the brain seems to be expended. . . .

During the first six or seven years of a child's life, special attention should be given to its physical training, rather than to the intellect. After this period, if the physical constitution is good, the education of both should receive attention. . . . Parents, especially mothers, should be the only teachers of such infant minds. They should not educate from books. The children generally will be inquisitive to learn the things of nature. They will ask questions in regard to the things they see and hear, and parents should improve the opportunity to instruct and patiently answer these little inquiries.— *H. to L., Chap. 2, pp. 42, 44.*

Hygiene of Motherhood.

636. It is an error generally committed to make no difference in the life of a woman previous to the birth of her children.— *T., V. II, p. 381.*

637. In past generations, if mothers had in-

formed themselves in regard to the laws of their being, they would have understood that their constitutional strength, as well as the tone of their morals, and their mental faculties, would in a great measure be represented in their offspring. Their ignorance upon this subject, where so much is involved, is criminal. Many women never should have become mothers. Their blood was filled with scrofula, transmitted to them from their parents, and increased by their gross manner of living. The intellect has been brought down and enslaved to serve the animal appetites, and children born of such parents have been poor sufferers, and of but little use to society. . . .

Wives and mothers who otherwise would have had a beneficial influence upon society in raising the standard of morals, have been lost to society through multiplicity of home cares, because of the fashionable, health-destroying manner of cooking, and also in consequence of too frequent child-bearing. They have been compelled to needless suffering, the constitution has failed, and the intellect has become weakened by so great a draught upon the vital resources. . . . If the mother, before the birth of her offspring, had always possessed self-control, realizing that she was giving the stamp of character to future generations, the present state of society would not be so depreciated in character as at the present time.

Every woman about to become a mother, whatever may be her surroundings, should encourage constantly a happy, cheerful, contented disposition, knowing that for all her efforts in this direction she will be repaid tenfold in the physical as well as the moral character of her offspring.— *H. to L., Chap. 2, pp. 37, 38.*

638. Great care should be exercised to have the surroundings of the mother pleasant and happy. . . . Not half the care is taken of some women while they are bearing children that is taken of animals in the stable.— *T., V. II, p. 383.*

639. The mother, in many cases previous to the **Tolling Mothers.** birth of her children, is permitted to toil early and late, heating her blood. . . . Her strength should have been tenderly cherished. . . . Her burdens and cares are seldom lessened, and that period, which should be to her of all others a time of rest, is one of fatigue, sadness, and gloom. By too great exertion on her part, she deprives her offspring of that nutrition which nature has provided for it, and by heating her own blood, she imparts to the child a bad quality of blood. The offspring is robbed of its vitality, robbed of physical and mental strength.— *H. to L., Chap. 2, p. 33.*

640. Many mothers, while nursing their infants, **Effect of the Mother's Overwork on the Infant.** have been permitted to overlabor, and to heat their blood in cooking, and the nurseling has been seriously affected, not only with fevered nourishment from the mother's breast, but its blood has been poisoned by the unhealthful diet of the mother. . . . The infant will also be affected by the condition of the mother's mind. If she is unhappy, easily agitated, irritable, giving vent to outbursts of passion, the nourishment the infant receives from its mother will be affected, often producing colic, spasms, and,

in some instances causing convulsions.— *H. to L .
Chap. 2, p. 39.*

Diet.

641. At this important period the labor of the
mother should be lightened. Great changes are
going on in her system. It requires a greater amount
of blood, and therefore an increase of food of the
most nourishing quality to convert into blood. Unless she has an abundant supply of nutritious food,
she cannot retain her physical strength, and her offspring is robbed of vitality. . . . There will be an
inability in the offspring to appropriate food which it
can convert into good blood to nourish the system.
. . . The extra draught upon the vitality of the
mother must be considered and provided for.— *T.,
V. II, pp. 381, 382.*

**Variable
Appetite.**

642. But, on the other hand, the idea that women,
because of their special condition, may let the appetite run riot, is a mistake based on custom, but
not on sound sense. The appetite of women in this
condition may be variable, fitful, and difficult to
gratify; and custom allows her to have anything she
may fancy, without consulting reason as to whether
such food can supply nutrition for her body and for
the growth of her child. The food should be nutritious, but should not be of an exciting quality.
Custom says that if she wants flesh meats, pickles,
spiced food, or mince pies, let her have them;
appetite alone is to be consulted. This is a great
mistake, and does much harm. The harm cannot
be estimated. If ever there is need of simplicity of
diet and special care as to the quality of food eaten,
it is at this important period. Women who possess

principle, and who are well instructed, will not depart from simplicity of diet at this time of all others. They will consider that another life is dependent upon them, and will be careful in all their habits, especially in diet.— *T., V. II, p. 382.*

643. From the food the mother was compelled to receive, she could not furnish a good quality of blood, and therefore gave birth to children filled with humors.— *T., V. II, p. 379.*

644. Her clothing also demands attention. Care should be taken to protect the body from a sense of chilliness. She should not call vitality unnecessarily to the surface to supply the want of sufficient clothing. . . . The prosperity of mother and child depends much upon good, warm clothing, and a supply of nourishing food.— *T., V. II, p. 382.* Clothing.

645. Very many children are born with their blood tainted with scrofula, through the wrong habits of the mother in her eating and dressing. The very many miscarriages that now occur may generally be traced to fashionable dress.— *H. R.*

Hygiene of the Sick-Room.

646. When we do all we can on our part to have health, then may we expect that blessed results will follow, and we can ask God in faith to bless our efforts for the preservation of health.— *H. to L., Chap. 4, p. 64.*

647. Thousands have died for want of pure water and pure air, who might have lived. . . . These blessings they need in order to become well. If they would become enlightened, and let medicine

alone, and accustom themselves to outdoor exercise, and to air in their houses, summer and winter, and use soft water for drinking and bathing purposes, they would be comparatively well and happy instead of dragging out a miserable existence.— *H. to L.*, *Chap. 4, p. 56.*

648. If those who are well need the blessing of light and air, and need to observe habits of cleanliness in order to remain well, the sick are in still greater need of them in proportion to their debilitated condition.— *H. to L.*, *Chap. 4, p. 60.*

Ventilation.   649. It is also of the greatest importance that the sick-room, from the first, be properly ventilated. This will be beneficial to the afflicted, and highly necessary to keep those well who are compelled to remain a length of time in the sick-room.— *H. to L.*, *Chap. 4, p. 54.*

650. There is a lamentable catalogue of evils which have their origin in the sick-room, from which the pure air of heaven is excluded. All who breathe this poisonous atmosphere violate the laws of their being, and must suffer the penalty.— *H. to L., Chap. 4, p. 58.*

651. Every breath of vital air in the sick-room is of the greatest value, although many of the sick are very ignorant on this point. They feel very much depressed, and do not know what the matter is. A draught of pure air through their room would have a happy, invigorating influence upon them. . . . The sick-room, if possible, should have a draught of air through it day and night. The draught should not

come directly upon the invalid.— *H. to L., Chap. 4, p. 59.*

652. In pleasant weather the sick in no case should be deprived of a full supply of fresh air. . . . Fresh air will prove more beneficial to the sick than medicine, and is far more essential to them than their food. They will do better and recover sooner deprived of food than of fresh air. . . . Their rooms may not always be so constructed as to allow the windows or doors to open in their rooms without the draughts coming directly upon them, and exposing them to take cold. In such cases windows and doors should be opened in an adjoining room, and thus let the fresh air enter the room occupied by the sick.— *H. to L., Chap. 4, p. 55.*

653. If no other way can be devised, the sick, if possible, should be removed to another room and another bed, while the sick-room, the bed and bedding, are being purified by ventilation.— *H. to L., Chap. 4, p. 60.*

654. It is of great value to the sick to have an even temperature in the room. This cannot always be correctly determined, if left to the judgment of the attendants, for they may not be the best judges of a right temperature. Some persons require more heat than others, and would be only comfortable in a room which to another would be uncomfortably warm. If each of these is at liberty to arrange the fires to suit her ideas of proper heat, the atmosphere in the sick-room will be anything but regular. . . . The friends of the sick, or attendants, who through anxiety and watching are deprived of sleep, and who

Temperature.

are suddenly awakened in the night from sleep to
attend in the sick-room, are liable to chilliness.
Such are not correct thermometers of the healthful
temperature of a sick-room. These things may appear of small account, but they have very much to
do with the recovery of the sick. In many instances
life has been imperiled by extreme changes of the
temperature of the sick-room.— *H. to L., Chap 4,
pp. 54, 55.*

655. While burning fevers are raging, there is but
little danger of taking cold. But especial care is
needful when the crisis comes, and fever is passing
away. Then constant watching may be necessary to
keep vitality in the system — *H. to L., Chap. 4,
p. 60.*

656. The heated, oppressed atmosphere, deprived
of vitality, benumbs the sensitive brain.— *T., V. I,
p. 702.*

Cleanliness.   657. If fevers enter a family, often more than
one have the same fever. This need not be if the
habits of the family are correct. If their diet is as
it should be, and they observe habits of cleanliness
and realize the necessity of ventilation, the fever
need not extend to another member of the family.
The reason that fevers prevail in families and expose
the attendants, is because the sick-room is not kept
free from poisonous infection, by cleanliness and
proper ventilation.— *H. to L., Chap. 4, p. 57.*

658. Many suffer decayed vegetable matter to remain about their premises. They are not awake to
the influence of these things. There is constantly
arising from these decaying substances an effluvium

that is poisoning the air; by inhaling the impure air, the blood is poisoned, the lungs become affected, and the whole system is diseased. Disease of almost every description will be caused by inhaling the atmosphere affected by these decaying substances.— *H. to L., Chap. 4, p. 61.*

659. All unnecessary noise and excitement should **Quiet.** be avoided in the sick-room, and the whole house should be kept as quiet as possible. Ignorance, forgetfulness, and recklessness have caused the death of many who might have lived had they received proper care from judicious, thoughtful attendants. The doors should be opened and shut with great care, and the attendants should be unhurried, calm, and self-possessed.— *H. to L., Chap. 4, p. 59.*

660. Much harm has resulted to the sick from the universal custom of having watchers at night. In critical cases this may be necessary; but it is often the case that more harm than good is done the sick by this practise. . . . Even one watcher will make more or less stir, which disturbs the sick. But where there are two, they often converse together, sometimes aloud, but more frequently in whispered tones, which is far more trying and exciting to the nerves of the sick than talking aloud. . . . Attendants upon the sick should, if possible, leave them to quiet and rest through the night, while they occupy a room adjoining. . . . The sick as a general thing are taxed with too many visitors and callers, who chat with them, and weary them by introducing different topics of conversation, when they need quiet and undisturbed rest. . . . It is a

mistaken kindness that leads so many, out of cour-
tesy, to visit the sick. Often have they spent a
sleepless, suffering night after receiving visitors.
They have been more or less excited, and the reaction has been too great for their already debilitated
energies, and as the result of these fashionable calls,
they have been brought into very dangerous conditions, and lives have been sacrificed for the want of
thoughtful prudence. . . . In very many instances
these fashionable calls have turned the scale when
the invalid was recovering, and the balance has
borne them down to death. Those who cannot
make themselves useful should be cautious in regard
to visiting the sick.— *H. to L., Chap. 4, p. 58.*

CHAPTER XXV.

THE ORGANS OF DIGESTION.

Physiology of the Digestive System.

661. The stomach has a controlling power upon the health of the entire body.— *H. R.*

662. Anything which is taken into the stomach and converted into blood becomes a part of the being.— *T., V. IV, p. 141.*

663. The benefit you derive from your food does not depend so much on the quantity eaten as on its thorough digestion, nor the gratification of the taste so much on the amount of food swallowed as on the length of time it remains in the mouth. . . . Eat slowly, and allow the saliva to mingle with the food. . . . Those who are excited, anxious, or in a hurry, cannot supply the necessary gastric juice.— *R. and H., 1884, No. 31.*

664. Thorough mastication is a benefit both to the teeth and the stomach.— *R. and H., 1883, No. 19.*

665. You are a nervous dyspeptic. The brain is closely connected with the stomach, and its power has so often been called to aid the weakened digestive organs that it is in its turn weakened, depressed, congested.— *T., V. II, p. 318.*

666. It is important that we relish the food we eat. If we cannot do this, but eat mechanically, we fail to be nourished and built up as we would be if we could enjoy the food we take into the stomach.— *T., V. I, p. 682.*

667. Immediately after eating there is a strong draught upon the nervous energy. The brain force is called into active exercise to assist the stomach; therefore, when the mind or body is taxed heavily after eating, the process of digestion is hindered. The vitality of the system, which is needed to carry on the work in one direction, is called away and set to work in another.— *T., V. II, p. 413.*

668. The stomach, when we lie down to rest, should have its work all done, that it may enjoy rest, as well as other portions of the body. The work of digestion should not be carried on through any period of the sleeping hours. After the stomach, which has been overtaxed, has performed its task, it becomes exhausted, which causes faintness. . . . The stomach becomes weary by being kept constantly at work. . . . Having no time for rest, the digestive organs become enfeebled, hence the sense of "goneness," and desire for frequent eating. . . . The stomach must have its regular periods for labor and rest.— *H. to L., Chap. 1, p. 56.*

Causes of Indigestion.

669. The stomach has a controlling power upon the health of the entire body. . . . The brain nerves are in strong sympathy with the stomach.— *H. R.*

670. Many are willingly ignorant of their own structure. They lead their children in the same path of selfish indulgence which they have followed, causing them to suffer the penalty of the transgression of nature's laws. They go to distant countries to seek a better climate, but their stomachs will create for them a malarious atmosphere wherever they may locate. They bring upon themselves sufferings that no one can alleviate.— *U. T., Aug. 25, 1897.*

Hasty Eating.

671. In order to have healthy digestion, food should be eaten slowly. Those who wish to avoid dyspepsia, and those who realize their obligation to keep all their powers in the condition which will enable them to render the best service to God, will do well to remember this. If your time to eat is limited, do not bolt your food, but eat less, and eat slowly. . . . Those who are excited, anxious, or in a great hurry would do well not to eat until they have found rest or relief; for the vital powers, already severely taxed, cannot supply the necessary gastric juice. . . . Eat slowly, and allow the saliva to mingle with the food.— *R. and H., 1884, No. 31.*

Drinking at Meals.

672. Food should not be washed down; no drink is needed with meals. . . . The more liquid there is taken into the stomach with meals, the more difficult it is for the food to digest; for the liquid must first be absorbed. . . . Many make a mistake in drinking cold water with their meals. Taken with meals, water diminishes the flow of the salivary glands; and the colder the water, the greater the injury to the stomach. Ice-water or iced lemonade, drunk with meals, will arrest digestion until the system has im-

parted sufficient warmth to the stomach to enable it
to take up its work again.— *Ibid.*

673. Hot drinks are debilitating; and besides,
those who indulge in their use become slaves to the
habit. . . . But if anything is needed to quench
thirst, pure water drunk some little time before or
after the meal is all that nature requires. Never
take tea, coffee, beer, wine, or any spirituous liquor.
Water is the best liquid possible to cleanse the
tissues.— *Ibid.*

Liquid Foods. 674. Soups, puddings, and other articles of the
kind are often eaten too hot, and as a consequence
the stomach is debilitated. Let them become partly
cooled before they are eaten.— *Ibid.*

675. To eat largely of porridge would not insure
health to the digestive organs; for it is too much
like liquid.— *Y. I., May 31, 1894.*

676. For those who can use them, good vegetables,
prepared in a healthful manner, are better than
soft mushes or porridge.— *U. T., Jan. 11, 1897.*

**Too Fre-
quent
Eating.** 677. A second meal should never be eaten until the
stomach has had time to rest from the labor of digesting the preceding meal.— *H. to L., Chap. 1, p. 55.*

678. After the stomach has done its work for one
meal, do not crowd more work upon it before it has
had a chance to rest, and to provide a sufficient
supply of gastric juice for the next meal. Five
hours at least should be given between each meal,
and always bear in mind that if you would give it a
trial, you would find that two meals would be better
than three.— *U. T., Aug. 30, 1896.*

679. If a third meal be eaten at all, it should be light, and several hours before going to bed. But with many the poor tired stomach may complain of weariness in vain. More food is forced upon it, which sets the digestive organs in motion, again to perform the same round of labor through the sleeping hours. The sleep is generally disturbed with unpleasant dreams, and in the morning they awake unrefreshed. There is a sense of languor and loss of appetite. A lack of energy is felt through the entire system. In a short time the digestive organs are worn out, for they have had no time to rest. Such persons become miserable dyspeptics, and wonder what has made them so. The cause has brought the sure result. If this practise is indulged in a great length of time, the health will become seriously impaired. The blood becomes impure, the complexion sallow, and eruptions will frequently appear. You will often hear complaints of frequent pains and soreness in the region of the stomach; and while performing labor, the stomach becomes so tired that they are obliged to desist from work, and rest. They seem to be at a loss to account for this state of things; for, setting this aside, they are apparently healthy. . . . After the stomach, which has been overtaxed, has performed its task, it is exhausted, which causes faintness. Here many are deceived, and think that it is the want of food that produces such feelings, and without giving the stomach time to rest, they take more food, which for the time removes the faintness. . . .

The stomach becomes weary by being kept constantly at work disposing of food not the most healthful. Having no time for rest, the digestive organs become enfeebled, hence the sense of "goneness" and desire for frequent eating.— *H. to L.*, *Chap. 1, p. 55.*

680. Gluttonous feasts, and food taken into the stomach at untimely seasons, leave an influence upon every fiber of the system.— *H. R.*

Improper Food Combinations.

681. The less that condiments and desserts are placed upon our tables, the better it will be for all who partake of the food. All mixed and complicated foods are injurious to the health of human beings. Dumb animals would never eat such a mixture as is often placed in the human stomach. . . . Rich and complicated mixtures of food are health destroying.— *U. T., Nov. 5, 1896.*

682. Because it is the fashion, in harmony with morbid appetite, rich cake, pies, and puddings, and every hurtful thing are crowded into the stomach. The table must be loaded down with variety or the depraved appetite cannot be satisfied. In the morning, these slaves to appetite often have impure breath and a furred tongue. They do not enjoy health, and wonder why they suffer with pains, headaches, and various ills. The cause has brought the sure result.— *H. to L., Chap. 1, p. 57.*

683. If we would preserve the best health, we should avoid eating vegetables and fruit at the same meal. If the stomach is feeble, there will be distress, the brain will be confused, and unable to put

forth mental effort. Have fruit at one meal and vegetables at the next.— *Y. I., May 31, 1894.*

684. I frequently sit down to the tables of the brethren and sisters and see that they use a great amount of milk and sugar. These clog the system, irritate the digestive organs, and affect the brain. Anything that hinders the active motion of the living machinery, affects the brain very directly. And from the light given me, sugar, when largely used, is more injurious than meat.— *T., V. II, p. 370.*

685. Nearly all the members of the human family **Overeating** eat more than the system requires. This excess decays, and becomes a putrid mass. . . . If more food, even of a simple quality, is placed in the stomach than the living machinery requires, this surplus becomes a burden. The system makes desperate efforts to dispose of it, and this extra work causes a tired feeling. Some who are continually eating call this "all gone" feeling hunger, but it is caused by the overworked condition of the abused digestive organs.— *U. T., Aug. 30, 1896.*

686. They (ministers, students, etc.) closely apply their minds to books, and eat the allowance of a laboring man. Under such habits, some grow corpulent, because the system is clogged. Others become lean, feeble, and weak, because their vital powers are exhausted in throwing off the excess of food; the liver becomes burdened, and unable to throw off the impurities in the blood, and sickness is the result.— *T., V. III, p. 490.*

687. Often this intemperance is felt at once in the form of headache and indigestion and colic. A load

has been placed upon the stomach that it cannot care for, and a feeling of oppression comes. The head is confused, the stomach is in rebellion. But these results do not always follow overeating. In some cases the stomach is paralyzed. No sensation of pain is felt, but the digestive organs lose their vital force. The foundation of the human machinery is gradually undermined, and life is rendered very unpleasant.—*U. T., Aug. 30, 1896.*

688. The power of the brain is lessened by drawing so heavily upon it to help the stomach get along with its heavy burden.— *T., V. II, p. 363.*

689. The brain nerve energy is benumbed and almost paralyzed by overeating— *T., V. II, p. 414.*

Improper Clothing.

690. The compression of the waist hinders the process of digestion. The heart, liver, lungs, spleen, and stomach are crowded into a small compass, not allowing room for the healthful action of these organs.—*H. R.*

691. When the extremities are not properly clad, the blood is chilled back from its natural course, and thrown upon the internal organs, breaking up the circulation and producing disease. The stomach has too much blood, causing indigestion.—*T., V. II, p. 531.*

Intemperance.

692. Intemperance in eating, even of food of the right quality, will have a prostrating influence upon the system. . . . Strict temperance in eating and drinking is highly essential for the healthy preservation and vigorous exercise of all the functions of the body. . . . Intemperance commences at our tables, in the use of unhealthful food. After a time, through

continued indulgence, the digestive organs become weakened, and the food taken does not satisfy the appetite. Unhealthy conditions are established, and there is a craving for more stimulating food.— *T.*, *V. III, p. 487.*

Helpful Suggestions as to Treatment.

693. The stomach must have its regular periods Regular for labor and rest. . . . With regular habits and Habits. proper food, the stomach will gradually recover. . . . Efforts should be made to preserve carefully the remaining strength of the vital forces, by lifting off every overtasking burden. The stomach may never fully recover health, but a proper course of diet will save further debility, and many will recover more or less, unless they have gone too far in gluttonous self-murder.— *H. to L., Chap. 1, p. 57.*

694. A second meal should never be eaten until the stomach has had time to rest from the labor of digesting the preceding meal.— *H. to L., Chap. 1, p. 55.*

695. The stomach becomes weary by being kept constantly at work; the remedy such require is to eat less frequently and less liberally, and be satisfied with plain, simple food, eating twice, or, at most, three times a day.— *H. to L., Chap. 1, p. 56.*

696. The stomach must have careful attention. It Rest. must not be kept in continual operation. Give this misused and much-abused organ some peace and quiet rest.— *U. T., Aug. 30, 1896.*

697. Exercise will aid the work of digestion. To Exercise. walk out after a meal, hold the head erect, put back

the shoulders, and exercise moderately, will be a great benefit. . . . The diseased stomach will find relief by exercise.— *T., V. II, p. 530.*

Air.

698. He has not had the vitalizing air of heaven to help in the work of digestion.— *T., V. II, p. 374.*

699. Pure, fresh air . . . excites the appetite, renders the digestion of food more perfect, and induces sound, sweet sleep.— *T., V. I, p. 702.*

Bathing.

700. Bathing helps the bowels, stomach, and liver, giving energy and new life to each. It also promotes digestion, and instead of the system's being weakened, it is strengthened.— *T., V. III, pp. 70, 71.*

Mental Influence.

701. The less the attention is called to the stomach after a meal, the better. If you are in constant fear that your food will hurt you, it most assuredly will. Forget self, and think of something cheerful. — *T., V. II, p. 530.*

702. At meal-time cast off all care and taxing thought. Do not be hurried, but eat slowly and with cheerfulness, your heart filled with gratitude to God for all his blessings.— *G. W., p. 174.*

703. You eat too much, and then you are sorry, and so you keep thinking upon what you eat and drink. Just eat that which is for the best, and go right away, feeling clear in the sight of Heaven and not having remorse of conscience.— *T., V. III, p. 374.*

CHAPTER XXVI.

THE LUNGS AND RESPIRATION.

Physiology of Respiration.

704. The health of the entire system depends upon the healthy action of the respiratory organs.— *H. to L., Chap. 6, p. 57.*

705. In order to have good blood, we must breathe well.—*H. R.*

706. The lungs, in order to be healthy, must have pure air.— *H. to L., Chap. 4, p. 63.*

707. Your lungs, deprived of air, will be like a hungry person deprived of food. Indeed, we can live longer without food than without air, which is the food that God has provided for the lungs.— *T., V. II, p. 533.*

708. The strength of the system is, in a great degree, dependent upon the amount of pure, fresh air breathed. If the lungs are restricted, the quantity of oxygen received into them is also limited, the blood becomes vitiated, and disease follows.—*H. R.*

709. It is impossible to go out in the bracing air of a winter's morning without inflating the lungs.— *T., V. II, p. 529.*

710. The compression of the waist by tight lacing prevents the waste matter from being thrown off through its natural channels. The most important of these is the lungs. In order for the lungs to do

the work designed, they must be left free, without the slightest compression. If the lungs are cramped, they cannot develop; but their capacity will be diminished, making it impossible to take a sufficient inspiration of air. The abdominal muscles were designed to aid the lungs in their action. Where there is no compression of the lungs, the motion in full breathing will be observed to be mostly of the abdomen. . . . When tight lacing is practised, the lower part of the chest has not sufficient room for action. The breathing, therefore, is confined to the upper portion of the lungs, where there is not sufficient room to carry on the work. But the lower part of the lungs should have the greatest freedom possible. The compression of the waist will not allow free action of the muscles of the respiratory organs.— *H. R.*

Causes of Diseases of the Respiratory Organs.

Unhygienic Surroundings.   711. Many suffer decayed vegetable matter to remain about their premises. . . . There is constantly arising from these decaying substances an effluvium that is poisoning the air. By inhaling the impure air, the blood is poisoned, the lungs become affected, and the whole system is diseased.— *H. to L., Chap. 4, p. 61.*

712. If a house be built where water settles around it, remaining for a time and then drying away, a poisonous miasma arises, and fever and ague, sore throat, lung diseases, and fevers will be the result.— *H. to L., Chap. 4, p. 64.*

713. Especially in wet seasons the sleeping-rooms become damp, and those who sleep in the beds are troubled with rheumatism, neuralgia, and lung complaints, which generally end in consumption.— *H. to L., Chap. 4, p. 64.*

714. Many families suffer from sore throat, lung diseases, and liver complaints, brought upon them by their own course of action. . . . They keep their windows and doors closed, fearing they will take cold if there is a crevice to let in the air. They breathe the same air over and over, until it becomes impregnated with the poisonous impurities and waste matter thrown off from their bodies, through the lungs and the pores of the skin.— *H. to L., Chap. 4, p. 63.* **Poor Ventilation.**

715. For invalids who have feeble lungs, nothing can be worse than an overheated atmosphere.— *T., V. II, p. 527.*

716. The heated, oppressed atmosphere, deprived of vitality, benumbs the sensitive brain. The lungs contract, the liver is inactive.— *T., V. I, p. 702.*

717. Stomach, liver, lungs, and brain are suffering for want of deep, full inspirations of air, which would electrify the blood and impart to it a bright, lively color, and which alone can keep it pure, and give tone and vigor to every part of the living machinery. — *T., V. II, p. 67.* **Improper Breathing.**

718. Speaking from the throat, letting the words come out from the upper extremity of the vocal organs, all the time fretting and irritating them, is not the best way to preserve health or to increase the efficiency of these organs.— *T., V. II, p. 616.* **Improper Use of the Voice.**

719. Careful attention and training should be given to the vocal organs. They are strengthened by right use, but become enfeebled if improperly used. Their excessive use will, if often repeated, not only injure the organs of speech, but will bring an undue strain upon the whole nervous system. The delicate harp of a thousand strings becomes worn, gets out of repair, and produces discord instead of melody. . . . It is not necessary to talk in a loud voice or in a high key; this does great injury to the speaker. . . . The human voice is a precious gift of God; it is a power for good, and the Lord wants his servants to preserve its pathos and melody. The voice should be cultivated so as to promote its musical quality, that it may fall pleasantly upon the ear and impress the heart. But the vocal organs are strangely abused, greatly to the injury of the speaker and the discomfort of the hearers.— *Sp. T., No. 7, p. 9.*

720. They injure the throat and vocal organs . . . when it is not called for. . . . This is in consequence of the unnatural position of the body, and the manner of holding the head.— *T., V. II, p. 617.*

721. Your dislike for physical taxation, while talking and exercising your throat, makes you liable to disease of the throat and lungs. . . . You should not let the labor come upon the upper part of the vocal organs, for this will constantly wear and irritate them, and will lay the foundation for disease. The action should come upon the abdominal muscles; the lungs and throat should be the channel, but should not do all the work.— *T., V. III, p. 311.*

722. Many speak in a rapid way, and in a high, unnatural key; but if they continue such a practise, they will injure the throat and lungs, and as a result of continual abuse the weak and inflamed organs will become diseased in a serious way, and they will fall into consumption.— *C. E., p. 125.*

723. There is need that among our ministers careful attention should be given to the culture of the voice, or many will lie down in untimely graves. — *C. E., p. 133.*

724. The proper use of the vocal organs will bring benefit to the physical health, and increase your usefulness and influence.— *C. E., p. 132.*

Proper Use of the Voice.

725. The extremities are chilled. . . . The heart fails in its efforts, and the limbs become habitually cold; and the blood, which is chilled away from the extremities, is thrown back upon the lungs and brain, and inflammation and congestion of the lungs or the brain is the result. . . . If the limbs and feet could have the extra coverings usually put upon the shoulders, lungs, and heart, and healthy circulation be induced to the extremities, the vital organs would act their part healthfully, with only their share of clothing.

Improper Dress.

I appeal to you mothers, do you not feel alarmed and heart-sick by seeing your children pale and dwarfed, suffering with catarrh, influenza, croup, scrofulous swellings appearing upon the face and neck, inflammation and congestion of the lungs and brain? Have you studied from cause to effect? Leaving their arms and legs insufficiently protected has been the cause of a vast amount of disease and premature death.— *H. to L., Chap. 5, p. 72.*

726. It is essential to health that the chest should have room to expand fully, so that the lungs may be enabled to take full inspirations of air. Many who have died of consumption might have lived their allotted term of life had they dressed in accordance with the laws of their being. The strength of the system is, in a great degree, dependent upon the amount of fresh air breathed. If the lungs are restricted, the quantity of oxygen received into them is also limited, the blood becomes vitiated, and disease follows.— *H. R.*

727 The arms' being naked exposes the infant to constant cold, and congestion of lungs or brain. These exposures prepare the way for the infant to become sickly and dwarfed.— *H. to L., Chap. 5, p. 71.*

Immoderate Eating. 728. Catarrhal difficulties, kidney disease, headache, and heart troubles are the result of immoderate eating.— *U. T., Aug. 30, 1896.*

Liquor. 729. By the habitual use of sour cider many bring upon themselves permanent disease. Some die of consumption or fall under the power of apoplexy from this cause alone.— *R. and H., 1884, No. 31.*

Drugs. 730. Every poisonous preparation in the vegetable and mineral kingdoms, taken into the system, will leave its wretched influence, affecting the liver and lungs.— *F. of F., p. 140.*

Care of the Respiratory Organs.

Exercise. 731. Morning exercise, walking in the free, invigorating air of heaven, or cultivating flowers, small fruits, and vegetables, is necessary to a healthful circulation of the blood. It is the surest safeguard against colds, coughs, congestion of the brain, inflammation of the liver, the kidneys, and the lungs, and a hundred other diseases.— *H. R.*

732. A walk, even in winter, would be more beneficial to the health than all the medicine the doctors may prescribe. . . . There will be increased vitality, which is so necessary to health. The lungs will have needful action; for it is impossible to go out in the bracing air of a winter's morning without inflating the lungs.— *T., V. II, p. 529.*

733. The strength of the system is, in a great **Fresh Air** degree, dependent upon the amount of pure air breathed.— *H. R.*

734. In the cool of the evening it may be necessary to guard from chilliness by extra clothing, but they should give their lungs air.— *T., V. II, p. 527.*

735. Many labor under the mistaken idea that if they have taken cold, they must carefully exclude the outside air, and increase the temperature of their room until it is excessively hot. The system may be deranged, the pores closed by waste matter, and the internal organs suffering more or less inflammation, because the blood has been chilled back from the surface and thrown upon them. At this time of all others the lungs should not be deprived of pure, fresh air. If pure air is ever necessary, it is when any part of the system, as the lungs or stomach, is diseased.— *T., V. II, p. 530.*

736. Air is the free blessing of Heaven, calculated to electrify the whole system.— *T., V. I, p. 701.*

CHAPTER XXVII.

THE HEART AND BLOOD.

Physiology of the Circulatory System.

737. Perfect health depends upon perfect circulation.— *T., V. II, p. 531.*

738. The more active the circulation the more free from obstructions and impurities will be the blood. The blood nourishes the body. The health of the body depends upon the healthful circulation of the blood.— *H. R.*

739. At every pulsation of the heart, the blood should be propelled to the extremities quickly and easily in order to have health. . . . The current of human life is struggling to go its accustomed rounds, and should not be hindered in its circuit through the body by the imperfect manner in which women clothe their limbs.— *H. R.*

740. The limbs were not formed by our Creator to endure exposure, as was the face. The Lord provided the face with an immense circulation, because it must be exposed. He provided, also, large veins and nerves for the limbs and feet, to contain a large amount of the current of human life, that the limbs might be uniformly as warm as the body.— *T., V. II, p. 531.*

741. The limbs and feet have large arteries, to receive a large amount of blood, that warmth, nutri-

tion, elasticity, and strength may be imparted to them. But when the blood is chilled from these extremities, their blood-vessels contract, which makes the circulation of the necessary amount of blood in them still more difficult.— *H. R.*

742. The extremities are chilled, and the heart has thrown upon it double labor, to force the blood into these chilled extremities; and when the blood has performed its circuit through the body, and returned to the heart, it is not the same vigorous, warm current which left it. It has been chilled in its passage through the limbs. The heart, weakened by too great labor and poor circulation of poor blood, is then compelled to still greater exertion, to throw the blood to the extremities which are never as healthfully warm as other parts of the body. The heart fails in its efforts, and the limbs become habitually cold; and the blood, which is chilled away from the extremities, is thrown back upon the lungs and brain, and inflammation and congestion of the lungs or the brain is the result.— *H. to L.*, *Chap. 5, p. 72.*

743. The nerves control the circulation of the blood; . . . for instance, you are impressed that if you bathe, you will become chilly. The brain sends this intelligence to the nerves of the body, and the blood-vessels, held in obedience to your will, cannot perform their office and cause a reaction after the bath.— *T., V. III, p. 70.*

Nervous Control of the Circulatory System.

744. You have a determined will, which causes the mind to react upon the body, unbalancing the circulation, and producing congestion in certain or-

gans; and you are sacrificing health to your feelings.
— *T., No. 32, p. 66.*

745. The exercise of the brain in study without
corresponding physical exercise has a tendency to
attract the blood to the brain, and the circulation of
the blood through the system becomes unbalanced.
The brain has too much blood and the extremities
too little. — *T., V. III, p. 138.*

Causes of Diseases of the Blood and Circulation.

746. Those who are not in health have impurities
of the blood.— *T., V. III, p. 70.*

747. A bad circulation leaves the blood to become
impure, induces congestion of the brain and lungs,
and causes diseases of the heart, the liver, and the
lungs.— *H. R.*

748. By interrupting the circulation of the blood,
the entire system is deranged.— *H. R.*

749. The chief if not the only reason why many
become invalids is that the blood does not circulate
freely, and the changes in the vital fluid which are
necessary to life and health do not take place.
They have not given their bodies exercise nor their
lungs food, which is pure, fresh air; therefore it is
impossible for the blood to be vitalized, and it pursues its course sluggishly through the system.— *T.,
V. II, p. 525.*

750. Foul blood will surely becloud the moral and
intellectual powers, and arouse and strengthen the
baser passions of your nature.— *T., V. II, p. 404.*

Innutrition.   751. Flesh meats, butter, cheese, rich pastry,
spiced foods, and condiments are freely partaken

of by both old and young. . . . The blood-making organs cannot convert such things into good blood.— *C. T., p. 47.*

752. In order to make a good quality of blood, we must have the right kind of food, prepared in a right manner.— *T., V. I, p. 682.*

753. A poor quality of food, cooked in an improper manner, and insufficient in quantity, cannot make good blood. Flesh meats and rich food and an impoverished diet will produce the same results. — *T., V. II, p. 368.*

754. Anything which is taken into the stomach and converted into blood, becomes a part of the being. Children should not be allowed to eat gross articles of food, such as pork, sausage, spices, rich cakes, and pastry; for by so doing their blood becomes fevered, the nervous system unduly excited, and the morals are in danger of being affected.— *T., V. IV, p. 141.*

Errors in Diet.

755. Indulging in eating too frequently, and of too large quantities, overtaxes the digestive organs, and produces a feverish state of the system. The blood becomes impure, and then diseases of various kinds follow.— *F. of F., p. 133.*

756. Catarrhal difficulties, kidney disease, headache, and heart troubles are the result of immoderate eating.— *U. T., Aug. 30, 1896.*

757. Your health is greatly injured by overeating and eating at improper times. This causes a determination of the blood to the brain. . . . You are in danger of apoplexy; and if you continue to disobey

the laws of health, your life will be cut short suddenly.— *T.*, *V. IV*, *pp. 501, 502.*

758. The liver becomes burdened, and unable to
throw off the impurities in the blood, and sickness is
the result.— *T.*, *V. III*, *p. 490.*

759. While fever is raging, food may irritate and
excite the blood; but as soon as the strength of the
fever is broken, nourishment should be given in a
careful, judicious manner.— *T.*, *V. II*, *p. 384.*

Flesh Meats.   760. Flesh meats will depreciate the blood. Cook
meat with spices, and eat it with rich cakes and pies,
and you have a bad quality of blood. The system
is too heavily taxed in disposing of this kind of food.
— *T.*, *V. II*, *p. 368.*

761. The eating of flesh meats has made a poor
quality of blood and flesh. Your systems are in a
state of inflammation, prepared to take on disease.
You are liable to acute attacks of disease, and to
sudden death, because you do not possess the strength
of constitution to rally and resist disease.— *T.*, *V.
II*, *p. 61.*

762. When we feed on flesh, the juices of what we
eat pass into the circulation. . . . Thus a feverish condition is created, because the animals are diseased,
and . . . we plant the seeds of disease in our own
tissue and blood.—*U. T.*, *Nov. 5, 1896.*

Pork.   763. Subsisting mostly on highly seasoned animal
food produces a feverish state of the system, especially if pork is used freely. The blood becomes
impure, the circulation is not equalized.— *F. of F.*,
p. 126.

764. Pork, although one of the most common articles of diet, is one of the most injurious. God did not prohibit the Hebrews from eating swine's flesh merely to show his authority, but because it was not a proper article of food for man. It would fill the system with scrofula, and especially in that warm climate produce leprosy and disease of various kinds. . . . Swine's flesh, above all other flesh meats, produces a bad state of the blood. . . . It is impossible for the flesh of any living creature to be healthy when filth is its natural element, and when it feeds upon every detestable thing. The flesh of swine is composed of what they eat. If human beings eat their flesh, their blood and their flesh will be corrupted by impurities conveyed to them through the swine.— *H. to L.*, *Chap. 1, p. 58.*

765. Cancers, tumors, and inflammatory diseases are largely caused by meat eating. . . . Flesh diet cannot make good blood.— *U. T., Nov 5, 1896.*

766. If the lungs are restricted, the quantity of oxygen received into them is also limited, the blood becomes vitiated, and disease follows.— *H. R.*

Impure Air.

767. For fear of taking cold they persist from year to year in . . . living in an atmosphere almost destitute of vitality. It is impossible for this class to have a healthy circulation.— *T., V. II, p. 526.*

768. Such can test the matter, and be convinced of the unhealthy air in their close rooms, by entering them after they have remained a while in the open air. Then they can have some idea of the impurities they have conveyed to the blood through the inhalations of the lungs.— *H. to L., Chap. 4, p. 63.*

769. By inhaling the impure air, the blood is poisoned, the lungs become affected, and the whole system is diseased.— *H. to L.*, *Chap. 4*, *p. 61.*

Lack of Exercise.

770. Inaction of any of the organs of the body will be followed by decrease in size and strength of the muscles, and will cause the blood to flow sluggishly through the blood-vessels.— *T.*, *V. III, p. 76.*

771. The blood is not enabled to expel the impurities as it would if active circulation were induced by exercise.— *T.*, *V. II, p. 529.*

772. The exercise of the brain in study, without corresponding physical exercise, has a tendency to attract the blood to the brain, and the circulation of the blood through the system becomes unbalanced. — *T.*, *V. III, p. 138.*

Improper Clothing.

773. Parents who dress their children with their extremities naked, or nearly so, are sacrificing the life and health of their children to fashion. If these parts are not so warm as the body, the circulation is not equalized. . . . The blood is driven to the head, causing headache or nosebleed; or there is a sense of fulness about the chest; producing cough or palpitation of the heart, on account of too much blood in that locality; or the stomach has too much blood, causing indigestion. . . . The blood is chilled back from its natural course, and thrown upon the internal organs, breaking up the circulation and producing disease.— *T.*, *V. II, p. 531.*

774. Look at the tight-fitting waists of the dresses of these children. It is impossible for their lungs to have full action. The heart and liver cannot do their work, thus compressed. . . . Look at their limbs,

unclad except by the slight covering of cotton stock-
ings. . . . The air chills the limbs, the life current
is driven back from its natural course, and the limbs
are robbed of their proportion of blood. The blood,
which should be induced to the extremities by their
being properly clad, is thrown back upon the internal organs. There is too much blood in the head.
The lungs are congested or the liver is burdened; by
interrupting the circulation of the blood, the entire
system is deranged.— *H.. R.*

775. The artificial hair and pads covering the base
of the brain heat and excite the spinal nerves centering in the brain. The head should ever be kept
cool. The heat caused by these artificial coverings
induces the blood to the brain. The action of the
blood upon the lower or animal organs of the brain,
causes unnatural activity, tends to recklessness in
morals, and the mind and heart are in danger of being corrupted.— *H. R.*

776. The impurities of the body, if not allowed to
escape, are taken back into the blood, and forced
upon the internal organs.— *H. to L., Chap. 4, p. 60·* **Lack of Cleanliness.**

777. From the food the mother was compelled to
receive, she could not furnish a good quality of
blood, and therefore gave birth to children filled
with humors.— *T., V. II, p. 379.* **Heredity.**

778. The disease which the drug was given to
cure may disappear, but only to reappear in a new
form, such as skin diseases, ulcers, painful, diseased
joints, and sometimes in a more dangerous and
deadly form. The liver, heart, and brain are frequently affected by drugs, and often all these organs **Drugs.**

are burdened with disease. . . . These organs, which should be in healthy condition, are enfeebled, and the blood becomes impure.— *H. to L., Chap. 3, p. 61.*

How Improved.

Exercise. 779. The more we exercise, the better will be the circulation of the blood. . . . Those who accustom themselves to proper exercise in the open air, will generally have a good and vigorous circulation. — *T., V. II, p. 525.*

780. Brisk, yet not violent, exercise in the open air, with cheerfulness of spirits, will promote the circulation, giving a healthy glow to the skin, and sending the blood, vitalized by the pure air, to the extremities.— *T., V. II, p. 530.*

781. There is no exercise that can take the place of walking. By it the circulation of the blood is greatly improved.— *T., V. III, p. 78.*

782. Physical labor, a diversion from mental, will draw the blood from the brain. . . . The circulation of the blood will be better equalized. — *T., V. II, p. 569.*

Fresh Air. 783. In order to have good blood, we must breathe well.— *H. R.*

784. The influence of pure, fresh air is to cause the blood to circulate healthfully through the system. — *T., V. I, p. 702.*

785. The chief if not the only reason why many become invalids, is that the blood does not circulate freely, and the changes in the vital fluid which are necessary to life and health do not take place.

They have not given their bodies exercise nor their lungs food, which is pure, fresh air; therefore it is impossible for the blood to be vitalized, and it pursues its course sluggishly through the system.— *T., V. II, p. 525.*

786. Pure water to drink and fresh air to breathe **Water Drinking.** invigorate the vital organs, purify the blood, and help nature in her task of overcoming the bad conditions of the system.— *H. to L., Chap. 4, p. 55.*

787. Water is the best liquid possible to cleanse the tissues.— *R. and H., 1884, No. 31.*

788. To secure a good circulation of the current **Clothing.** of human life, all parts of the body must be suitably clad.— *H. R.*

789. Bathing frees the skin from the accumulation **Bathing.** of impurities which are constantly collecting, and keeps the skin moist and supple, thereby increasing and equalizing the circulation.— *T., V. III, p. 70.*

790. A bath, properly taken, fortifies against cold, because the circulation is improved, . . . for the blood is brought to the surface, and a more easy and regular flow of the blood through all the blood-vessels is obtained.— *T., V. III, p. 71.*

CHAPTER XXVIII.

THE SKIN AND ITS FUNCTIONS.

Physiology of the Skin.

Elimination. 791. Impurities are constantly and imperceptibly passing from the body, through the pores, and if the surface of the skin is not kept in a healthy condition, the system is burdened with impure matter.— *H. to L., Chap. 4, p. 60.*

792. The burden of labor is thrown upon the liver, lungs, kidneys, etc., and these internal organs are compelled to do the work of the skin.— *T., V. II, p. 524.*

793. The skin needs to be carefully and thoroughly cleansed, that the pores may do their work in freeing the body from impurities.— *T., V. III, p. 70.*

794. You have not given your body a chance to breathe. The pores of the skin, or the little mouths through which the body breathes, have become closed, and the system has been filled with impurities.— *T., V. III, p. 74.*

795. Its million little mouths are closed, because they are clogged by the impurities of the system, and for want of air.— *T., V. I, p. 701.*

796. They breathe the same air over and over, until it becomes impregnated with the poisonous impurities and waste matter thrown off from their

bodies through the lungs and the pores of the skin.
— *H. to L., Chap. 4, p. 63.*

797. If the garments worn are not frequently **Absorption.**
cleansed from these impurities, the pores of the
skin absorb again the waste matter thrown off. The
impurities of the body, if not allowed to escape, are
taken back into the blood, and forced upon the
internal organs.— *H. to L., Chap. 4, p. 60.*

798. Many are ignorantly injuring their health
and endangering their lives by using cosmetics. . . .
When they become heated, . . . the poison is absorbed by the pores of the skin, and is thrown into
the blood. Many lives have been sacrificed by this
means alone.— *H. R.*

Impaired Action of the Skin.

799. The surface of the skin is nearly dead because **Impure Air.**
it has no air to breathe. Its million little mouths are
closed, because they are clogged by the impurities of
the system, or for want of air.— *T., V. I, p. 701.*

800. The effects produced by living in close, ill-
ventilated rooms are these: . . . The body becomes
relaxed; the skin becomes sallow; digestion is retarded; and the system is peculiarly sensitive to the
influence of cold. A slight exposure produces serious
diseases. Great care should be exercised not to sit
in a draught or in a cold room when weary or when
in a perspiration.— *T., V. I, p. 702.*

801. For fear of taking cold they persist from year
to year in . . . living in an atmosphere almost
destitute of vitality. . . . The skin becomes debili-

tated, and more sensitive to any change in the atmosphere.— *T., V. II, p. 526.*

Improper Clothing.

802. Additional clothing is put on, and the heat of the room increased. The next day they require a little more heat and a little more clothing, in order to feel perfectly warm; and thus they humor every changing feeling until they have but little vitality to endure any cold. . . . If you add clothing, let it be but little, and exercise, if possible, to regain the heat you need.— *T., V. II, p. 526.*

803. You have worn too great an amount of clothing, and have debilitated the skin by so doing.— *T., V. III, p. 74.*

804. The unnatural heat caused by artificial hair and pads about the head, induces the blood to the brain, producing congestion, and causing the natural hair to fall off.— *H. R.*

Improper Diet.

805. With many the poor, tired stomach may complain of weariness in vain. More food is forced upon it, which sets the digestive organs in motion, again to perform the same round of labor. . . . These become miserable dyspeptics. . . . If this practise be indulged in for a great length of time, the health becomes seriously impaired. The blood becomes impure, the complexion sallow, and eruptions frequently appear.— *H. to L., Chap. 1, p. 55.*

Drugs.

806. This is the effect of calomel. . . . It frequently manifests itself in tumors, ulcers, and cancers, years after it has been introduced into the system.— *H. to L., Chap. 3, p. 59.*

807. The disease, which the drug was given to cure may disappear, but only to reappear in a new

form, such as skin diseases, ulcers, painful, diseased joints, and sometimes in a more dangerous and deadly form.— *H. to L., Chap. 3, p. 61.*

808. Ladies may resort to cosmetics to restore the tint of the complexion, but they cannot thus bring back the glow of healthful feelings to the heart. That which darkens and makes dingy the skin also clouds the spirits and destroys cheerfulness and peace of mind.— *H. R.*

Compensatory Action of the Internal Organs.

809. Those who are not in health have impurities in the blood, and the skin is not in a healthy condition.— *T., V. III, p. 70.*

810. The studied habit of shunning the air and avoiding exercise closes the pores,— the little mouths through which the body breathes,— making it impossible to throw off impurities through that channel. The burden of labor is thrown upon the liver, lungs, kidneys, etc., and these internal organs are compelled to do the work of the skin.— *T., V. II, p. 524.*

811. These pores have become clogged and cannot perform the task allotted to them, and so the internal organs have a double task thrown upon them, and the whole system is deranged.— *H. R.*

812. If you add clothing, let it be but little, and exercise, if possible, to regain the heat you need. If you positively cannot engage in active exercise, warm yourselves by the fire; but as soon as you are warm, lay off your extra clothing, and remove from the fire.— *T., V. II, p. 526.*   Treatment.

813. If those who can, would engage in some active employment to take the mind from themselves, they would generally forget that they were chilly, and would not receive harm.— *T., V. II, p. 526.*

814. Bathing frees the skin from the accumulation of impurities, which are constantly collecting, and keeps the skin moist and supple.— *T., V. III, p. 70.*

815. Twice a week she should take a general bath, as cool as will be agreeable, a little cooler every time, until the skin is toned up.— *T., V. I, p. 702.*

816. Upon rising in the morning, most persons would be benefited by taking a sponge bath, or, if more agreeable, a hand bath, with merely a washbowl of water; this will remove impurities from the skin.— *H. to L., Chap. 4, p. 63.*

817. Frequent bathing is very beneficial, especially at night just before retiring, or upon rising in the morning. It will take but a few moments to give the children a bath, and to rub them until their bodies are in a glow. This brings the blood to the surface, relieving the brain.— *C. T., p. 141.*

818. Bathe frequently in pure soft water, followed by gentle rubbing.—*H. to L., Chap. 3, p. 54.*

CHAPTER XXIX.

THE BRAIN AND THE NERVOUS SYSTEM.

The Physiology of the Nervous System.

819. Each faculty of the mind and each muscle has its distinctive office, and all require to be exercised in order to become properly developed and retain healthful vigor.— *T., V. III, p. 77.*

820. Every organ of the body was made to be servant of the mind.— *T., V. III, p. 136.*

821. The brain is the capital of the body, the seat of all the nervous forces and of mental action. The nerves proceeding from the brain control the body. By the brain nerves, mental impressions are conveyed to all the nerves of the body as by telegraph wires; and they control the vital action of every part of the system. All the organs of motion are governed by the communications they receive from the brain. — *T., V. III, p. 69.*

822. The senses . . . are the avenues to the soul. —*T., V. III, p. 507.*

823. The brain nerves which communicate with the entire system are the only medium through which Heaven can communicate with man, and affect his inmost life. Whatever disturbs the circulation of the electric currents in the nervous system, lessens the strength of the vital powers, and the result is a

deadening of the sensibilities of the mind.— *T., V. II, p. 347.*

824. Any part of the body that is not treated with consideration will telegraph its injury to the brain.— *C. E., p. 125.*

825. The nervous system, having been unduly excited, borrowed power for present use from its future resources of strength.— *T., V. III, p. 487.*

826. Anything that hinders the active motion of the living machinery, affects the brain very directly. — *T., V. II, p. 370.*

827. A calm, clear brain and steady nerve are dependent upon a well-balanced circulation of the blood.— *H. R.*

Examples of Nervous Control. 828. When the minds of ministers, school-teachers, and students are continually excited by study, and the body is allowed to be inactive, the nerves of emotion are taxed, while the nerves of motion are inactive.— *T., V. III, p. 490.*

829. Immediately after eating there is a strong draught upon the nervous energy. . . . Therefore, when the mind or body is taxed heavily after eating, the process of digestion is hindered. The vitality of the system, which is needed to carry on the work in one direction, is called away and set to work in another.— *T., V. II, p. 413.*

830. The very food they place before their children is such as to irritate the tender coats of the stomach. This excitement is communicated, through the nerves, to the brain, and the result is that the animal passions are aroused, and control the moral

powers.   Reason is thus made a servant to the lower qualities of the mind.— *T.*, *V. IV, p. 140.*

831. This drug poison, opium, gives temporary **Opium** relief from pain, but does not remove the cause of pain.   It only stupefies the brain, rendering it incapable of receiving impressions from the nerves.   While the brain is thus insensible, the hearing, the taste, and the sight are affected.   When the influence of opium wears off, and the mind arouses from its state of paralysis, the nerves, which have been cut off from communication with the brain, shriek out louder than ever . . . because of the additional outrage the system has sustained in receiving this poison.— *H. to L., Chap. 3, p. 56.*

Sympathetic Nervous Disturbances.

832. God himself has formed us with distinctive organs and faculties.   These he designs should act together in harmony.   If we injure one, all are affected.— *H. R.*

833. Every wrong habit which injures the health of the body, reacts in effect upon the mind.— *H. R.*

834. The brain is the citadel of the whole man, and wrong habits of eating, dressing, or sleeping affect the brain, and prevent the attaining of that which the student desires,— a good mental discipline.   Any part of the body that is not treated with consideration will telegraph its injury to the brain.— *C. E., p. 125.*

835. It is impossible for the brain to do its best work when the digestive powers are abused.   Many eat hurriedly of various kinds of food, which set up

a war in the stomach, and thus confuse the brain.
. . . At meal-time cast off care and taxing thought.
Do not be hurried, but eat slowly and with cheerfulness, your heart filled with gratitude to God for all his blessings; and do not engage in brain labor immediately after a meal. Exercise moderately, and give a little time for the stomach to begin its work.
— *G. W., p. 174.*

836. When the mind or body is taxed heavily after eating, the process of digestion is hindered. The vitality of the system, which is needed to carry on the work in one direction, is called away and set to work in another.— *T., V. II, p. 413.*

837. What the users of these stimulants call strength is only received by exciting the nerves of the stomach, which convey the irritation to the brain, and this in turn is aroused to impart increased action to the heart.— *T., V. II, p. 65.*

838. Those who are changing from three meals a day to two, will at first be troubled more or less with faintness, especially about the time they have been in the habit of eating the third meal. But if they persevere for a short time, this faintness will disappear.— *H. to L., Chap. 1, p. 56.*

Causes of Nervous Diseases.

839. Anything that hinders the active motion of the living machinery affects the brain very directly. — *T., V. II, p. 370.*

Unhealthful Surroundings. 840. It is destructive to the health and life of young children to sit in the schoolroom upon hard, ill-formed benches, from three to five hours a day, inhaling the impure air caused by many breaths. The weak lungs become affected, the brain, from which the nervous energy of the whole system is derived, becomes enfeebled by being called into active exercise before the strength of the mental organs is sufficiently matured to endure fatigue.— *H. to L.*, *Chap.* 2, *p.* 43.

841. In the schoolroom the foundation has been too surely laid for diseases of various kinds. But more especially the most delicate of all organs, the brain, has often been permanently injured by too great exercise. This has often caused inflammation, then dropsy of the head, and convulsions with their dreaded results. . . . In those children who have survived, the nervous energy of the brain becomes so weakened that after they come to maturity it is impossible for them to endure much mental exercise. The forces of some of the delicate organs of the brain seem to be expended.— *H. to L.*, *Chap.* 2, *p.* 43.

842. The mind which is allowed to be absorbed in story reading is being ruined. The practise results in air-castle building and a sickly sentimentalism. The imagination becomes diseased, and there is a vague unrest, a strange appetite for unwholesome mental food. Thousands are to-day in insane asylums whose minds became unbalanced by novel reading.— *S. of T.*, *1884, No. 41.* **Abuse of the Mind**

843. The memory is greatly injured by ill-chosen reading, which has a tendency to unbalance the reasoning powers, and to create nervousness, weariness of the brain, and prostration of the entire system.— *T.*, *V. IV*, *p.* 497.

844. The exercise of the brain in study, without corresponding physical exercise, has a tendency to attract the blood to the brain, and the circulation of the blood through the system becomes unbalanced. The brain has too much blood, and the extremities too little.— *C. E., p. 9.*

845. Minds are often abused, and goaded on to madness by pursuing one line of thought; the excessive employment of the brain power and the neglect of the physical creates diseased conditions of the system.— *Sp. Instr. on Ed. Work, p. 14.*

846. Doubt, perplexity, and excessive grief often sap the vital forces, and induce nervous disease of a most debilitating and distressing character.— *R. and H., 1881, No. 43.*

Irregular Habits.

847. The mind does not wear out or break down so often on account of diligent employment and hard study, as on account of eating improper food at improper times, and of careless inattention to the laws of health. . . . Diligent study is not the principal cause of the breaking down of the mental powers. The main cause is improper diet, irregular meals, and a lack of physical exercise. Irregular hours for eating and sleeping sap the brain forces.— *Y. I., May 31, 1894.*

Insufficient Air.

848. Stomach, liver, lungs, and brain are suffering for the want of deep, full inspirations of air.— *T., V. II, p. 67.*

Improper Dress.

849. Artificial hair and pads covering the base of the brain, heat and excite the nerves centering in the brain. . . . The heat caused by these artificial coverings induces the blood to the brain, producing

congestion.   In consequence of the brain's being congested its nerves lose their healthy action.— *H. R.*

850. Their limbs, as well as their arms, are left almost naked. . . . The heart, weakened by too great labor, fails in its efforts, and the limbs become habitually cold; and the blood, which is chilled away from the extremities, is thrown back upon the lungs and brain, and inflammation and congestion of the lungs or the brain is the result.— *H. to L.*, *Chap. 5, pp. 71, 72.*

851. The brain is closely connected with the stomach, and its power has so often been called to aid the weakened digestive organs that it is in its turn weakened, depressed, congested.— *T., V. II, p. 318.*

Errors in Diet.

852. The brain-nerve energy is benumbed and almost paralyzed by overeating.— *T., V. II, p. 414.*

853. Your health is greatly injured by overeating and eating at improper times.   This causes a determination of the blood to the brain.   The mind becomes confused, and you have not the proper control of yourself.   You appear like a man whose mind is unbalanced.   You make strong moves, are easily irritated, and view things in an exaggerated and perverted light.— *T., V. IV, p. 501.*

854. If the stomach is burdened with too much food, even of a simple character, the brain force is called to the aid of the digestive organs.   There is a benumbed sensation upon the brain.   It is almost impossible to keep the eyes open. . . . The brain is almost paralyzed in consequence of the amount of food eaten.— *T., V. II, p. 603.*

855. Nature bears abuse as long as she can without resisting, then she arouses and makes a mighty effort to rid herself of the incumbrances and evil treatment she has suffered. Then come headache, chills, fever, nervousness, paralysis, and other evils too numerous to mention.—*T., V. II, p. 69.*

856. Children should not be allowed to eat gross articles of food, such as pork, sausage, spices, rich cakes, and pastry; for by so doing their blood becomes fevered, the nervous system unduly excited, and the morals are in danger of being affected.— *T., V. IV, p. 141.*

857. Some animals that are brought to the slaughter seem to realize what is to take place, and they become furious, and literally mad. They are killed while in this state, and their flesh prepared for market. Their meat is poison, and has produced in those who have eaten it, cramps, convulsions, apoplexy, and sudden death.— *H. to L., Chap. 1, p. 60.*

Stimulants. 858. The appetite for liquor is encouraged by the preparation of food with condiments and spices. These cause a feverish state of the system. . . . The effect of such food is to cause nervousness.— *R. and H., 1883, No. 44.*

859. To a certain extent tea produces intoxication. . . . Tea draws upon the strength of the nerves, and leaves them greatly weakened. . . . When the system is already overtaxed and needs rest, the use of tea spurs up nature by stimulation to unwonted, unnatural action, and thereby lessens her power to perform and her ability to endure; and her powers give out long before Heaven designed they should.

Tea is poisonous to the system. . . . The second effect of tea drinking is headache, wakefulness, palpitation of the heart, indigestion, trembling of the nerves, and many other evils.— *T.*, *V. II, p. 64.*

860. The influence of coffee is in a degree the same as tea, but the effect upon the system is still worse. Its influence is exciting, and just in the degree that it elevates above par, it will exhaust and bring prostration below par. . . . The relief obtained from them [tea and coffee] is sudden, before the stomach has had time to digest them. This shows that what the users of these stimulants call strength is only received by exciting the nerves of the stomach, which convey the irritation to the brain, and this in turn is aroused to impart increased action to the heart, and short-lived energy to the entire system. All this is false strength, that we are the worse for having.— *T.*, *V. II, p. 65.*

861. Tobacco is a poison of the most deceitful and malignant kind, having an exciting, then a paralyzing, influence upon the nerves.— *F. of F., p. 128.*

862. Tobacco-using is a habit which frequently affects the nervous system in a more powerful manner than does the use of alcohol.— *T.*, *V. III, p. 562.*

863 While it [tobacco] acts upon some [infants who are compelled to inhale its fumes] as a slow poison, and affects the brain, heart, liver, and lungs, and they waste away and fade gradually, upon others it has a more direct influence, causing spasms, paralysis, and sudden death.— *H. to L., Chap. 5, p. 68*

864. A tendency to disease of various kinds, as dropsy, liver complaint, trembling nerves, and a determination of blood to the head, results from the habitual use of sour cider. . . . Some die of consumption or fall under the power of apoplexy from this cause alone.— *R. and H., 1884, No. 13.*

Drugs. 865. The drugs given to stupefy, whatever they may be, derange the nervous system.— *H. to L., Chap. 3, p. 57.*

866. The liver, heart, and brain are frequently affected by drugs, and often all these organs are burdened with disease, and the unfortunate subjects, if they live, are invalids for life, wearily dragging out a miserable existence.— *H. to L., Chap. 3, p. 61.*

867. Witness the mildest protracted influence of nux vomica upon the human system. At its introduction, the nervous energy was excited to extraordinary action to meet this drug poison. This extra excitement was followed by prostration, and the final result has been paralysis of the nerves.— *H. to L., Chap. 3, p. 58.*

868. Poisonous medicines, or something called a soothing cordial, . . . is poured down the throat of the abused infant. . . . If it recovers, it must bear about more or less in its system the effects of that poisonous drug, and it is liable to spasms, heart disease, dropsy of the brain, or consumption. Some infants are not strong enough to bear even a trifle of drug poisons; and as nature rallies to meet the intruder, the vital forces of the tender infant are too severely taxed, and death ends the scene.— *H. to L., Chap. 5, p. 70.*

869. Impure thoughts lead to impure actions. *Vice.*
. . . Some . . . are in danger of paralysis of the
brain. Already the moral and intellectual powers
are weakened and benumbed.— *T., V. II, pp. 408,
409.*

870. Many sink into an early grave, while others
have a sufficient force of constitution to pass this
ordeal. . . . Nature will make them pay the penalty
for the transgression of her laws . . . by numerous
pains in the system, . . . neuralgia, . . . affection
of the spine.— *S. A., pp. 63, 64.*

Treatment for Nervous Disorders.

871. The mind and body are intimately connected. *Improve
the General
Health.* If the former is to be firm and well balanced, the latter should be in the best possible condition. Conscience and right principles of life should be sustained
by firm, quiet nerves, a healthy circulation, and the
activity and strength of general health.— *H. R.*

872. Air, air, the precious boon of heaven, which *Fresh Air.*
all may have, will bless you with its invigorating
influence if you will not refuse it entrance. Welcome it, cultivate a love for it, and it will prove a
precious soother of the nerves. . . . It refreshes the
body, . . . while at the same time its influence is
decidedly felt upon the mind, imparting a degree of
composure and serenity. . . . It induces sound,
sweet sleep.— *T., V. I, p. 702.*

873. You were in danger of being stricken down *Diet.*
by paralysis, one half of you becoming dead. A
denial of appetite is salvation to you.— *T., V. I, p.
546.*

874. All these brethren need to adhere more strictly and perseveringly to a healthful, spare diet, for all are in danger of congested brains, and paralysis may fell one or more or all of them, if they continue living carelessly or recklessly.— *T., V. I, p. 588.*

875. You should use the most simple food, prepared in the most simple manner, that the fine nerves of the brain be not weakened, benumbed, or paralyzed.— *T., V. II, p. 46.*

Exercise. 876. Healthy, active exercise is what you need. This will invigorate the mind. Neither study nor violent exercise should be engaged in immediately after a full meal.— *T., V. II, p. 413.*

877. Physical labor, a diversion from mental, will draw the blood from the brain.— *T., V. II, p. 569.*

878. Morning exercise, in walking in the free, invigorating air of heaven, . . . is the surest safeguard against colds, coughs, congestions of the brain and lungs, . . . and a hundred other diseases.— *H. R.*

879. The proper exercise of mind and body will develop and strengthen all the powers. Both mind and body will be preserved, and will be capable of doing a variety of work. . . . The proper use of the physical strength as well as the mental powers, will equalize the circulation of the blood, and keep every organ of the living machinery in running order. . . . Every faculty of the mind may be exercised with comparative safety if the physical powers are equally taxed, and the subject of thought varied. We need

a change of employment, and nature is a living, healthful teacher.— *Sp. Instr. on. Ed. Work, p. 14.*

880. The bath is a soother of the nerves.— *T.,* **The Bath.** *V. III, p. 70.*

881. Some . . . have a powerful will, which, ex- **Mental** ercised in the right direction, would be a potent **Influence.** means of controlling the imagination and thus resisting disease.— *T., V. II, p. 524.*

882. You are capable of controlling your imagination and overcoming these nervous attacks. You have will power, and you should bring it to your aid.— *T., No. 32, p. 66.*

883. Bring to your aid the power of the will, which will resist cold and will give energy to the nervous system.— *T., V. II, p. 533.*

884. The consciousness of right-doing is the best medicine for diseased bodies and minds.— *T., V. I, p. 502.*

885. The Bible is a soother of the nerves, and **The Bible.** imparts solidity of mind and firm principles.— *R. and H., 1878, Nov. 28.*

CHAPTER XXX.

AUTO-INTOXICATION, OR SELF-POISONING.

886. The more active the circulation, the more free will be the blood from obstructions and impurities.— *H. R.*

Toxins Generated. 887. Impurities are constantly and imperceptibly passing from the body through the pores, and if the skin is not kept in a healthy condition, the system is burdened with impure matter. If the garments worn are not frequently cleansed from these impurities, the pores of the skin absorb again the waste matter thrown off. The impurities of the body, if not allowed to escape, are taken back into the blood, and forced upon the internal organs. Nature, to relieve herself of poisonous impurities, makes an effort to free the system, which effort produces fevers and what is termed disease.— *H. to L., Chap. 4, p. 60.*

888. Many families suffer with sore throat, and lung diseases, and liver complaints, brought upon them by their own course of action. . . . They keep their windows and doors closed, fearing they will take cold if there is a crevice open to let in the air. They breathe the same air over and over until it becomes impregnated with the poisonous impurities and waste matter thrown off from their bodies through the lungs and the pores

of the skin. These impurities are conveyed to the blood through the inhalations of the lungs.— *H. to L.*, *Chap. 4, p. 63.*

889. Many are made sick by the indulgence of appetite. . . . So many varieties are introduced into the stomach that fermentation is the result. This condition brings on acute disease, and death frequently follows.— *U. T., Aug. 25, 1897.*

890. If physical exercise were combined with mental exertion, the blood would be quickened in its circulation, the action of the heart would be more perfect, impure matter would be thrown off, and new life and vigor would be experienced in every part of the body. . . . They closely apply their minds to books, and eat the allowance of a laboring man. Under such habits some grow corpulent, because the system is clogged. Others become lean, feeble, and weak, because their vital powers are exhausted in throwing off the excess of food ; the liver becomes burdened and unable to throw off the impurities in the blood, and sickness is the result.— *T., V. III, p. 490.*

891. The studied habit of shunning the air and avoiding exercise closes the pores, . . . making it impossible to throw off impurities through that channel. The burden of labor is thrown upon the liver, lungs, kidneys, etc., and these internal organs are compelled to do the work of the skin. Thus persons bring diseases upon themselves by their wrong habits.— *T., V. II, p. 524.*

Defective Elimination.

CHAPTER XXXI.

COLDS.

892. Many labor under the mistaken idea that if they have taken cold, they must carefully exclude the outside air, and increase the temperature of their room until it is excessively hot. The system may be deranged, the pores closed by waste matter, and the internal organs suffering more or less inflammation, because the blood has been chilled back from the surface and thrown upon them.— *T., V. II, p. 530.*

893. The effects produced by living in close, ill-ventilated rooms are these: . . . The body becomes relaxed; the skin becomes sallow; digestion is retarded, and the system is peculiarly sensitive to the influence of cold. A slight exposure produces serious diseases. Great care should be exercised not to sit in a draught or in a cold room when weary, or when in a perspiration.— *T., V. I, p. 702.*

894. If the child has taken cold, it is generally due to the wrong management of the mother. If its head is covered as well as its body while sleeping, in a short time it will be in a perspiration, caused by labored breathing, because of the lack of pure, vital air. When it is taken from beneath the covering, it is almost sure to take cold. The arms' being naked exposes the infant to constant cold, and congestion of the lungs or brain. These exposures prepare the

way for the infant to become sickly and dwarfed.—
H. to L., Chap. 5, p. 71.

895. When we overtax our strength, and become
exhausted, we are liable to take cold, and at such
times there is danger of disease's assuming a dangerous form.— *T., V. III, p. 13.*

896. When the extremities, which are remote from **Clothing.**
the vital organs, are not properly clad, the blood is
driven to the head, causing headache or nosebleed;
or there is a sense of fulness about the chest, producing cough or palpitation of the heart, on account
of too much blood in that locality.— *T., V. II,
p. 531.*

897. An abundance of clothing about the chest,
where is the great wheel of life, induces the blood to
the lungs and brain, and produces congestion.—
H. R.

898. A dress thus long gathers dew from the grass,
. . . and in its bedraggled condition it comes in
contact with the sensitive ankles, which are not sufficiently protected, quickly chilling them, and is one
of the greatest causes of catarrh and of scrofulous
swelling, and endangers health and life.— *H. to L.,
Chap. 6, p. 62.*

899. Drug takers are never well. They are always
taking cold, which causes extreme suffering, because
of the poison all through their system.— *F. of F.,
p. 137.*

900. At this time, of all others, the lungs should **Helpful**
not be deprived of pure, fresh air. If pure air is **Hints
Concerning**
ever necessary, it is when any part of the system, as **Colds.**
the lungs or stomach, is diseased. Judicious exer-

14

cise would induce the blood to the surface, and thus relieve the internal organs. Brisk, yet not violent, exercise in the open air, with cheerfulness of spirits, will promote the circulation, giving a healthy glow to the skin, and sending the blood, vitalized by the pure air, to the extremities.— *T., V. II, p. 530.*

901. Bring to your aid the power of the will, which will resist cold, and will give energy to the nervous system.— *T., V. II, p. 533.*

902. Instead of increasing the liability to cold, a bath, properly taken, fortifies against cold, because the circulation is improved, . . . for the blood is brought to the surface, and a more easy and regular flow of blood through all the blood-vessels is obtained.— *T., V. III, p. 71.*

903. Morning exercise, in walking in the free invigorating air of heaven, . . . is the surest safeguard against colds, coughs, congestions of the brain and lungs, . . . and a hundred other diseases.— *H. R.*

904. Twice a week she should take a general bath, as cool as will be agreeable, a little cooler every time, until the skin is toned up.— *T., V. I, p. 702.*

CHAPTER XXXII.

FEVERS AND ACUTE DISEASES.

Causes of Acute Diseases.

905. Nature is burdèned and endeavors to resist your efforts to cripple her. Chills and fevers are the result of those attempts to rid herself of the burden you lay upon her.— *T., V. II, p. 68.*

906. Nature, to relieve herself of poisonous impurities, makes an effort to free the system, which effort produces fevers and what is termed disease.— *H. to L., Chap. 4, p. 60.*

907. Nature bears abuse as long as she can without resisting, then she arouses, and makes a mighty effort to rid herself of the incumbrances and evil treatment she has suffered. Then come headache, chills, fevers, nervousness, paralysis, and other evils too numerous to mention.— *T., V. II, p. 69*

908. When we feed on flesh, the juices of what we **Diet.** eat pass into the circulation. A feverish condition is created, because the animals are diseased; and by partaking of their flesh we plant the seeds of disease in our own tissue and blood. Then, when exposed to the changes in a malarious atmosphere, to epidemics and contagious diseases, the system feels their effects; it is not in a condition to resist disease.— *U. T., Nov. 5, 1896.*

909. Highly seasoned animal food produces a feverish state of the system; especially if pork is used freely, the blood becomes impure, the circulation is not equalized, and chills and fever follow.— *F. of F.*, *p. 126.*

910. Many times your children have suffered from fever and ague brought on by improper eating, when their parents were accountable for their sickness.— *T.*, *V. IV*, *p. 502.*

911. Children should not be allowed to eat gross articles of food, such as pork, sausage, spices, rich cakes, and pastry; for by so doing their blood becomes fevered.— *T.*, *V. IV*, *p. 141.*

912. Thousands have indulged their perverted appetites, have eaten a good meal, as they call it, and as the result have brought on a fever or some other acute disease, and certain death.— *T.*, *V. II*, *p. 69.*

Ventilation. 913. The effects produced by living in close, ill-ventilated rooms are these : The system becomes weak and unhealthy, the circulation is depressed, the blood moves sluggishly through the system because it is not purified and ventilated by the pure, invigorating air of heaven. The mind becomes depressed and gloomy, while the whole system is enervated, and fevers and other acute diseases are liable to be generated.— *T.*, *V. I*, *pp. 702, 703.*

Infection. 914. If fevers enter a family, often more than one have the same fever. This need not be if the habits of the family are correct. If their diet is as it should be, and they observe habits of cleanliness, and realize the necessity of ventilation, the fever need not extend to another member of the family. The reason that fevers prevail in families, exposing the attendants, is because the sick-room is not kept free from poisonous infection by cleanliness and proper ventilation.— *H. to L., Chap. 4, p. 57.*

915. Families have been afflicted with fevers, some have died, and the remaining portion of the family circle have almost murmured against their Maker because of their distressing bereavements, when the sole cause of all their sickness and death has been the result of their own carelessness. The impurities about their own premises have brought upon them contagious diseases. . . . Disease of almost every description will be caused by inhaling the atmosphere affected by these decaying substances. There is constantly arising from them an effluvium that is poisoning the air.— *F. of F., p. 141.*

916. If a house be built where water settles around it, remaining for a time and then drying away, a poisonous miasma arises, and fever and ague, sore throat, lung diseases, and fevers will be the result.— *H. to L., Chap. 4, p. 64.*

917. In nine cases out of ten the indisposition of children can be traced to some indulgence of the perverted appetite. Perhaps it is an exposure to cold, want of fresh air, irregularity in eating, or improper clothing; and all the parents need to do is to remove the cause, and secure for their children a period of quiet and rest or abstinence for a short time from food. An agreeable bath, of the proper temperature, will remove impurities from the skin, Helpful Suggestions.

and the unpleasant symptoms may soon disappear.
— *H. R.*

918. Reduce the feverish state of the system by a
careful and intelligent application of water. These
efforts will help nature in her struggle to free the
system of impurities. . . . The use of water can
accomplish but little if the patient does not feel the
necessity of also strictly attending to his diet.—
H. to L., Chap. 3, p. 60.

919. If, in their fevered state, water had been
given them to drink freely, and applications had
also been made externally, long days and nights of
suffering would have been saved, and many precious
lives spared. But thousands have died with raging
fevers consuming them, until the fuel which fed the
fever was burned up, the vitals consumed, and have
died in the greatest agony, without being permitted
to have water to allay their burning thirst. Water,
which is allowed a senseless building to put out the
raging elements, is not allowed human beings to put
out the fire which is consuming the vitals.— *H. to L.,
Chap. 3, p. 62.*

920. The blessed, heaven-sent water, skilfully applied, would quench the devouring flame, but it is
set aside for poisonous drugs.— *T., No. 31, p. 191.*

921. In cases of severe fever, abstinence from
food for a short time will lessen the fever, and
make the use of water more effectual. But the
acting physician needs to understand the real condition of the patient, and not allow him to be
restricted in diet for a great length of time until
his system becomes enfeebled. While the fever is

raging, food may irritate and excite the blood; but as soon as the strength of the fever is broken, nourishment should be given in a careful, judicious manner. If food is withheld too long, the stomach's craving for it will create fever, which will be relieved by a proper allowance of food of the right quality. It gives nature something to work upon. If there is a great desire expressed for food, even during the fever, to gratify that desire with a moderate amount of simple food would be less injurious than for the patient to be denied. When he can get his mind upon nothing else, nature will not be overburdened with a small portion of simple food.— *T., V. II, pp. 384, 385.*

922. The sick-room, if possible, should have a draught of air through it day and night. The draught should not come directly upon the invalid. While burning fevers are raging, there is but little danger of taking cold. But especial care is needful when the crisis comes, and the fever is passing away. Then constant watching may be necessary to keep vitality in the system.— *H. to L., Chap. 4, pp. 59, 60.*

CHAPTER XXXIII.

MORAL MALADIES.

General Statements. 923. Immorality abounds everywhere. Licentiousness is the special sin of the age. Never did vice lift its deformed head with such boldness as now.— *T., V. II, p. 346.*

924. A lethargy of unconscious sensualism, through indulgence of a perevrted appetite, a constant submitting of soul and body and spirit to moral defilement, is upon the people. . . . And these lustful appetites, with their destroying power, have been transmitted from parents to children, and so intensified that the names of those who bear them are recorded in the books of heaven as transgressors of God's law.— *U. T., Jan. 11, 1897.*

925. Moral pollution has done more than every other evil to cause the race to degenerate. It is practised to an alarming extent, and brings on disease of almost every description. Even very small children, infants, being born with natural irritability of the sexual organs, find momentary relief in handling them, which only increases the irritation, and leads to a repetition of the act, until a habit is established which increases with their growth. These children, generally puny and dwarfed, are prescribed for by physicians, and drugged; but

[216]

the evil is not removed. The cause still exists. — *T.*,
V. II, p. 391.

926. Many might have been saved if they had
been carefully instructed in regard to the influence
of this practise upon their health. They were ignorant of the fact that they were bringing much suffering
upon themselves. — *S. A., p. 55.*

Inducing Causes of Immorality.

927. If ever there was a time that the diet should **Diet.**
be of the most simple kind, it is now. Meat should
not be placed before our children. Its influence is
to excite and strengthen the lower passions, and has
a tendency to deaden the moral powers. . . . The
less feverish the diet, the more easily can the passions
be controlled. — *T.*, *V. II, p. 352.*

928. You place upon your tables butter, eggs, and
meat, and your children partake of them. They are
fed with the very things that will excite their animal
passions, and then you come to meeting and ask
God to bless and save your children. — *T.*, *V. II,
p. 362.*

929. The very food they place before their children is such as to irritate the tender coats of the
stomach. This excitement is communicated, through
the nerves, to the brain, and the result is that the
animal passions are aroused, and control the moral
powers. — *T.*, *V. IV, p. 140.*

930. By indulging in a wrong course of eating and
drinking, thousands upon thousands are ruining their
health, and not only is their health ruined, but their

morals are corrupted, because diseased blood flows through their veins.— *U. T., Aug. 30, 1896.*

Idleness.

931. To relieve the young from healthful labor is the worst possible course a parent can pursue. Their life is then aimless, the mind and hands unoccupied, the imagination active, and left free to indulge in thoughts that are not pure and healthful. In this condition they are inclined to indulge still more freely in that vice which is the foundation of all their complaints. . . . Some mothers with their own hands open the door and virtually invite the devil in, by permitting their children to remain in idleness.— *S. A., p. 58.*

Wicked Associates.

932. Children who are experienced in this vice seem to be bewitched by the devil until they can impart their vile knowledge to others.— *S. A., p. 54.*

933. Neighbors may permit their children to come to your house, to spend the evening and the night with your children. Here is a trial, and a choice for you, to run the risk of offending your neighbors by sending their children to their own homes, or gratify them, and let them lodge with your children, and thus expose them to be instructed in that knowledge which would be a lifelong curse to them.— *S. A., p. 56.*

934. If you are situated so that their intercourse with young associates cannot always be overruled as you would wish to have it, then let them visit your children in your presence, and in no case allow these associates to lodge in the same bed, or even in the same room. It will be far easier to prevent an evil than to cure it afterward.— *S. A., p. 58.*

Remedial Agencies.

935. Mothers, it is a crime for you to allow yourselves to remain in ignorance in regard to the habits of your children. If they are pure, keep them so. Fortify their young minds, and prepare them to detest this health-and-soul-destroying vice. Shield them from becoming contaminated by associating with every young companion.— *S. A., p. 58.* **Fortify Minds against Evil.**

936. The less feverish the diet, the more easily can the passions be controlled.— *T., V. II, p. 352.* **Regulate the Diet.**

937. Give your children physical labor, which will call into exercise the nerves and the muscles. The weariness attending such labor will lessen their inclination to indulge in vicious habits. Idleness is a curse. It produces licentious habits.—*T., V. II, p. 349.* **Useful Labor.**

938. Active employment will give but little time to invite Satan's temptations. They may be often weary, but this will not injure them. Nature will restore their vigor and strength in their sleeping hours, if her laws are not violated. And the thoroughly tired person has less inclination for secret indulgence.— *S. A., p. 62.*

Results of Impure Habits.

939. Moral pollution has done more than any other evil to cause the race to degenerate. . . It brings on disease of almost every description.— *T., V. II, p. 391.*

940. Industry does not weary and exhaust one fifth part as much as the pernicious habit of self-abuse.— *T., V. II, p. 349.*

941. Secret indulgence is, in many cases, the only real cause of the numerous complaints of the young. This vice is laying waste the vital forces and debilitating the system; and until the habit which produced the result is broken off, there can be no permanent cure.— *S. A.*, *p. 58*.

Physical Effects.

942. The sensitive nerves of the brain have lost their healthy tone by morbid excitation to gratify an unnatural desire for sensual indulgence.— *T.*, *V. II*, *p. 347*.

943. Let us view the results of this vice upon the physical strength. Have you not marked the lack of healthy beauty, of strength and power of endurance, in your dear children? Have you not felt saddened as you watched the progress of disease upon them, which has baffled your skill and that of physicians? You listen to numerous complaints of headache, catarrh, dizziness, nervousness, pain in the shoulders and side, loss of appetite, pain in the back and limbs, wakeful, feverish nights, tired feelings in the morning, and great exhaustion after exercising. As you have seen the beauty of health disappearing, and have marked the sallow countenance or the unnaturally flushed face, have you been aroused sufficiently to look beneath the surface, to inquire into the cause of this physical decay? Have you observed the astonishing mortality among the youth?— *S. A.*, *p. 49*.

944. In those who indulge in this corrupting vice before attaining their growth, the evil effects are more plainly marked, and recovery from its effects is more nearly hopeless. The frame is weak and

stunted, the muscles are flabby; the eyes become small, and appear at times swollen; the memory is treacherous, and becomes sieve-like; and the inability to concentrate the thoughts upon study increases.— *T., V. II, p. 402.*

945. The young indulge to quite an extent in this vice before the age of puberty, without experiencing at the time, to any very great degree, the evil results upon the constitution. But at this critical period, while merging into manhood and womanhood, nature makes them feel the previous violation of her laws.— *S. A., p. 57.*

946. Many sink into an early grave, while others have sufficient force of constitution to pass this ordeal. If the practise is continued from the age of fifteen and upwards, nature will protest against the abuse she has suffered and continues to suffer, and will make them pay the penalty of the transgression of her laws, especially from the ages of thirty to forty-five, by numerous pains in the system, and various diseases, such as affection of the liver and lungs, neuralgia, rheumatism, affection of the spine, diseased kidneys, and cancerous humors. . . . There is often a sudden breaking down of the constitution; and death is the result.— *S. A., pp. 63, 64.*

947. Have you not noticed that there was a deficiency in the mental health of your children? that their course seemed to be marked with extremes? that they were absent-minded? that they started nervously when spoken to, and were easily irritated? Have you not noticed that, when occupied upon a piece of work, they would look dreamingly, as though

Mental Effects.

the mind was elsewhere? And when they came to
their senses, they were unwilling to own the work as
coming from their hands, it was so full of mistakes,
and showed such marks of inattention. Have you
not been astonished at their wonderful forgetfulness?
The most simple and oft-repeated directions would
often be forgotten. They might be quick to learn,
but it would be of no special benefit to them; the
mind would not retain it. What they might learn
through hard study, when they would use their knowledge, is missing, lost through their sieve-like mem-
ories. Have you not noticed their reluctance to
engage in active labor, and their unwillingness to
perseveringly accomplish that which they have under-
taken, which taxes the mental as well as the physical
strength? — *S. A.*, *p. 50.*

948. Have you not witnessed the gloomy sadness
upon the countenance, and frequent exhibitions of
a morose temper in those who once were cheerful,
kind, and affectionate? They are easily excited to
jealousy, disposed to look upon the dark side, and
when you are laboring for their good, imagine that
you are their enemy, that you needlessly reprove and
restrain them. — *S. A.*, *p. 50.*

Moral Effects. 949. And have you inquired, Where will all this
end? as you have looked upon your children from
a moral point of view? Have you not noticed the
increase of disobedience in your children, and their
manifestations of ingratitude and impatience under
restraint? Have you not been alarmed at their
disregard of parental authority, which has bowed
down the heart of their parents with grief, and

prematurely sprinkled their heads with gray hair?
Have you not witnessed the lack of that noble
frankness in your children which they once possessed, and which you admired in them? Some
children even express in their countenances a hard-
ened look of depravity. Have you not felt distressed and anxious as you have seen the strong
desire in your children to be with the other sex,
and their overpowering disposition to form attach-
ments when quite young? . . . Mothers, the great
cause of these physical, mental, and moral evils is
secret vice, which inflames the passions, fevers the
imagination, and leads to fornication and adultery.
This vice is laying waste the constitution of very
many, and preparing them for diseases of almost
every description.— *S. A.*, *p. 53.*

950. Upon their very countenances is imprinted
the sin of Sodom. A continuance of these sins will
bring the sure and terrible results. They will suddenly be destroyed, and that without remedy. They
will receive the sentence, " He that is unjust, let
him be unjust still; and he which is filthy, let him
be filthy still." — *U. T.*, *Jan. 11, 1897.*

CHAPTER XXXIV.

RATIONAL REMEDIES FOR DISEASE.

Efforts of Nature to Resist Disease.

951. Nature alone possesses restorative powers. She alone can build up her exhausted energies, and repair the injuries she has received by inattention to her fixed laws.— *H. to L., Chap. 3, p. 57.*

952. Nature alone is the effectual restorer.— *H. to L., Chap. 3, p. 60.*

953. Nature, to relieve herself of poisonous impurities, makes an effort to free the system, which effort produces fevers, and what is termed disease.— *H. to L., Chap. 4, p. 60.*

954. Nature bears abuse as long as she can without resisting, then she arouses, and makes a mighty effort to rid herself of the incumbrances and evil treatment she has suffered. Then come headache, chills,. fevers, nervousness, paralysis, and other evils too numerous to mention.— *T., V. II, p. 69.*

955. Nature is loath to give up her hold on life. She is unwilling to cease her struggle.— *H. to L., Chap. 3, p. 63.*

956. Give nature a chance, and she will rally and again perform her part nobly and well.— *T., V. I, p. 549.*

957. Nature was doing her best to rid the system of an accumulation of impurities, and could she have been left to herself, aided by the common

blessings of Heaven, such as pure air and pure water, a speedy and safe cure would have been effected.— *H. to L., Chap. 3, p. 60.*

958. All the credit should be ascribed to nature's restorative power.— *H. to L., Chap. 3, p. 50.*

959. Only seek to assist nature in her efforts, by removing every obstruction, and then leave her to recover the exhausted energies of the system.— *H. to L., Chap. 3, p. 54*

Assistance We May Render Nature.

960. There are many ways of practising the healing art; but there is only one way that Heaven approves. God's remedies are the simple agencies of nature, that will not tax or debilitate the system through their powerful properties. Pure air and water, cleanliness, a proper diet, purity of life, and a firm trust in God are remedies for the want of which thousands are dying; yet these remedies are going out of date because their skilful use requires work that the people do not appreciate. Fresh air, exercise, pure water, and clean, sweet premises are within the reach of all with but little expense.— *T., No. 32, p. 199.*

961. Keep the patient free from excitement, and every influence calculated to depress. Her attendants should be cheerful and hopeful. She should have a simple diet, and should be allowed plenty of pure, soft water to drink. Bathe frequently in pure, soft water, followed by gentle rubbing. Let the light and air be freely admitted into the room. She must have quiet and undisturbed rest.— *H. to L., Chap. 3, pp. 54, 55.*

15

Water Drinking.

962. Water is the best liquid possible to cleanse the tissues. . . . Drink some little time before or after the meal.—*R. and H., 1884, No. 31.*

963. Fast for one or two meals, and drink only pure, soft water. The loss of a meal or two will enable the overburdened system to overcome slight indispositions; and even graver difficulties may sometimes be overcome by this simple process.—*H. R.*

964. Their sallow skins indicate that they are bilious. . . . Observe regular habits of rising early. . . . Eat sparingly, thus relieving the system of unnecessary burden, and encourage cheerfulness; take proper exercise in the open air, bathe frequently, and drink freely of pure, soft water.—*H. R.*

965. If they would become enlightened, . . . and accustom themselves to outdoor exercise, and to air in their houses, summer and winter, and use soft water for drinking and bathing purposes, they would be comparatively well and happy, instead of dragging out a miserable existence.—*H. to L., Chap. 4, p. 56.*

Bathing.

966. Many have never experienced the beneficial effects of water, and are afraid to use one of heaven's greatest blessings.— *H. to L., Chap. 3, p. 62.*

967. The use of water can accomplish but little if the patient does not feel the necessity of also strictly attending to his diet.— *H. to L., Chap. 3, p. 60.*

968. Persons in health should . . . by all means bathe as often as twice a week. Those who are not in health have impurities of the blood. . . . The skin needs to be carefully and thoroughly cleansed, that the pores may do their work in freeing the body from impurities; therefore feeble persons who are diseased surely need the advantages and blessings of bathing as often as twice a week, and frequently even more thàn this is positively necessary.— *T., V. III, p. 70.*

Frequency of the Bath.

969. Frequent bathing is very beneficial, especially at night just before retiring, or upon rising in the morning.—*C. T., p. 141.*

970. A bath, properly taken, fortifies against cold, because the circulation is improved ; . . . for the blood is brought to the surface, and a more easy and regular flow of the blood through all the blood-vessels is obtained.— *T., V. III, p. 71.*

Manner of Giving the Bath.

971. Reduce the feverish state of the system by a careful and intelligent application of water.— *H. to L., Chap. 3, p. 60.*

972. If, in their fevered state, water had been given them to drink freely, and applications had also been made externally, long days and nights of suffering would have been saved, and many precious lives spared.— *H. to L., Chap. 3, p. 62.*

973. The fire of fever seems consuming him. He longs for pure water to moisten the parched lips, to quench the raging thirst, and to cool the fevered brow. . . . The blessed, heaven-sent water, skilfully applied, would quench the devouring flame.— *T., No. 31, p. 191.*

974. Twice a week she should take a general bath, as cool as will be agreeable, a little cooler every time, until the skin is toned up.— *T., V. I, p. 702.*

975. It will take but a few moments to give the children a bath and to rub them until their bodies are in a glow.— *C. T., p. 141.*

Effects of the Bath. 976. Whether a person is sick or well, respiration is more free and easy if bathing is practised. By it the muscles become more flexible, the body and mind are alike invigorated, the intellect is made brighter, and every faculty becomes livelier. The bath is a soother of the nerves. It promotes general perspiration, quickens the circulation, overcomes obstructions in the system, and acts beneficially on the kidneys and the urinary organs. Bathing helps the bowels, stomach, and liver, giving energy and new life to each. It also promotes digestion, and instead of the system's being weakened, it is strengthened. Instead of increasing the liability to cold, a bath, properly taken, fortifies against cold, because the circulation is improved, and the uterine organs, which are more or less congested, are relieved; for the blood is brought to the surface, and a more easy and regular flow of the blood through all the blood-vessels is obtained.— *T., V. III, p. 70.*

977. Nature, to relieve herself of poisonous impurities, makes an effort to free the system, which effort produces fevers and what is termed disease. But even then, if those who are afflicted would assist nature in her efforts by the use of pure, soft water, much suffering would be prevented.— *H. to L., Chap. 4, p. 60.*

Sunlight.

978. This is one of nature's most healing agents. —*T., V. II, p. 527.*

979. If you would have your homes sweet and inviting, make them bright with air and sunshine, remove your heavy curtains, open the windows, throw back the blinds, and enjoy the rich sunlight, even if it be at the expense of the colors of your carpets. —*T., V. II, p. 527.*

980. If the windows were freed from blinds and heavy curtains, and the air and sun permitted to enter freely the darkened rooms, there would be seen a change for the better in the mental and physical health of the children. The pure air would have an invigorating influence upon them, and the sun that carries healing in its beams would soothe and cheer, and make them happy, joyous, and healthy.— *H. R.*

981. The confined air of unventilated rooms meets us with sickening odors of mildew and mold, and the impurities exhaled from its inmates. . . . The emanations from damp, moldy rooms and clothing are poisonous to the system. . . . If all would appreciate the sunshine, and expose every article of clothing to its drying, purifying rays, mildew and mold would be prevented. . . . This is the only way rooms can be kept from impurities. . . . Every room in our dwellings should be daily thrown open to the healthful rays of the sun, and the purifying air should be invited in. This will be a preventive of disease.— *H. R.*

982. Exercise, and a free and abundant use of the air and sunlight, . . . would give life and strength to the emaciated.—*T., V. II, p. 531.*

983. The feeble one should press out into the sunshine as earnestly and naturally as do the shaded plants and vines. The pale and sickly grain blade that has struggled up out of the cold of early spring, puts out the natural and healthy deep green after enjoying for a few days the health-and-life-giving rays of the sun. Go out into the light and warmth of the glorious sun, you pale and sickly ones, and share with vegetation its life-giving, health-dealing power. —*H. R.*

Relation of the Mind to the Body.

984. But few realize the power the mind has over the body.— *T., V. III, p. 184.*

985. The sympathy which exists between the mind and the body is very great; when one is affected, the other responds.— *T., V. IV, p. 60.*

986. The burden of sin, with its unrest and unsatisfied desires, lies at the very foundation of a large share of the maladies which the sinner suffers.— *T., V. IV, p. 579.*

987. Sickness of the mind prevails everywhere. Nine tenths of the diseases from which men suffer have their foundation here. Perhaps some living home trouble is, like a canker, eating to the very soul and weakening the life forces. Remorse for sin sometimes undermines the constitution and unbalances the mind.— *T., No. 32, p. 200.*

988. Great wisdom is needed . . . in order to cure the body through the mind. But few realize the power that the mind has over the body. A great deal of the sickness which afflicts humanity has its origin in the mind, and can only be cured by restoring the mind to health. There are very many more than we imagine who are sick mentally. To deal with men and women whose minds as well as bodies are diseased, is nice work.— *T., V. III, p. 184.* Help for the Body through the Mind.

989. Thousands are sick and dying around us who might get well and live if they would; but their imagination holds them. They fear that they will be made worse if they labor or exercise, when this is just the change they need to make them well. Without this, they never can improve. They should exercise the power of the will, rise above their aches and debility, and engage in useful employment, and forget that they have aching backs, sides, lungs, and heads.— *T., V. III, p. 76.* Influence of the Will.

990. I have met many who were really sufferers through their imagination. They lacked will power to rise above and combat disease of body and mind; and therefore they were held in suffering bondage.— *H. R.*

991. You have a determined will, which causes the mind to react upon the body, unbalancing the circulation, and producing congestion in certain organs; and you are sacrificing health to your feelings. . . . And yet you are capable of controlling your imagination, and overcoming these nervous attacks. — *T., No. 32, p. 66.*

992. The nerves . . control the vital action of every part of the system. If your mind is impressed and fixed that a bath will injure you, the mental impression is communicated to all the nerves of the body. The nerves control the circulation of the blood; therefore the blood is, through the impression of the mind, confined to the blood-vessels, and the good effects of the bath are lost. All this is because the blood is prevented by the mind and will from flowing readily, and from coming to the surface to stimulate, arouse, and promote the circulation. For instance, you are impressed that if you bathe you will become chilly. The brain sends this intelligence to the nerves of the body, and the blood-vessels, held in obedience to your will, cannot perform their office and cause a reaction after the bath. —*T., V. III, p. 70.*

993. Let the mind become intelligent, and the will be placed on the Lord's side, and there will be a wonderful improvement in the physical health. But this can never be accomplished in mere human strength.— *M. M., V. II, p. 216.*

994. Keep the power of the will awake; for the will, aroused and rightly directed, is a potent soother of the nerves.— *T., V. I, p. 557.*

995. Bring to your aid the power of the will, which will resist cold, and will give energy to the nervous system.— *T., V. II, p. 533.*

Cheerfulness Productive of Health. 996. A contented mind, a cheerful spirit, is health to the body and strength to the soul. Nothing is so fruitful a cause of disease as depression, gloominess, and sadness.— *T., V. I, p. 702.*

997. That which brings sickness of body and mind to nearly all is dissatisfied feelings and discontented repinings.— *T., V. I, p. 566.*

998. Heart-sickness makes many dyspeptics; for mental trouble has a paralyzing influence upon the digestive organs.— *T., V. III, p. 184.*

999. The less the attention is called to the stomach after a meal, the better. If you are in constant fear that your food will hurt you, it most assuredly will.̄ — *T., V. II, p. 530.*

1000. We should encourage a cheerful, hopeful, peaceful frame of mind; for our health depends upon our so doing.— *T., V. III, p. 13.*

1001. Cheerfulness and a clear conscience are better than drugs, and will be an effective agent in your restoration to health.— *H. R.*

1002. You who are suffering with poor health, there is a remedy for you. If thou clothe the naked, and bring the poor that are cast out to thy house, and deal thy bread to the hungry, "then shall thy light break forth as the morning, and thine health shall spring forth speedily." Doing good is an excellent remedy for disease.— *T., V. II, p. 29.*

Doing Good a Remedy for Disease.

1003. The consciousness of right-doing is the best medicine for diseased bodies and minds. He who is at peace with God has secured the most important requisite to health. The blessing of the Lord is life to the receiver.— *S. of T., 1882, No. 23.*

1004. The condition of the mind has much to do with the health of the physical system. If the mind is free and happy, under a consciousness of right-doing and a sense of satisfaction in causing happiness to others, it will create a cheerfulness that will react upon the whole system, causing a freer circulation of the blood and a toning up of the entire body. — *T., V. IV, p. 60.*

1005. Doing good is a work that benefits both giver and receiver. If you forget self in your interest for others, you gain a victory over your infirmities. The satisfaction you will realize in doing good will aid you greatly in the recovery of the healthy tone of the imagination. The pleasure of doing good animates the mind and vibrates through the whole body.— *T., V. II, p. 534.*

1006. The blessing of God is a healer; and those who are abundant in benefiting others, will realize that wondrous blessing in their hearts and lives.— *T., V. IV, p. 60.*

Restorative Power of the Spirit of God.

1007. The influence of the Spirit of God is the very best medicine for disease. Heaven is all health; the more deeply heavenly influences are realized, the more sure will be the recovery of the believing invalid.— *C. T., p. 13.*

1008. Sickness of the mind prevails everywhere. Nine tenths of the diseases from which men suffer have their foundation here. . . . The religion of Christ, so far from being the cause of insanity, is one of its most effectual remedies; for it is a potent soother of the nerves.— *T., No. 32, p. 200.*

1009. In nine cases out of ten the knowledge of a sin-pardoning Saviour would make them better both in mind and body.— *T., No. 32, p. 205.*

1010. Many carry a violated conscience, and can be reached only by the principles of Bible religion. — *T., V. III, p. 168.*

1011. A sore, sick heart, a discouraged mind, needs mild treatment; and it is through tender sympathy that this class of minds can be healed. The physician should first gain their confidence, and then point them to the all-healing Physician. If their minds can be directed to the Burden-Bearer, and they can have faith that he will have an interest in them, the cure of their diseased bodies and minds will be sure. — *T., V. III, p. 184.*

1012. A person whose mind is quiet and satisfied in God is in the pathway to health. — *R. and H., 1880, No. 11.*

1013. The assurance of God's approval will promote physical health. It fortifies the soul against doubt, perplexity, and excessive grief, that so often sap the vital forces and induce nervous diseases of a most debilitating and distressing character. — *R. and H., 1883, No. 41.*

1014. The exalting influence of the Spirit of God is the best restorative for the sick. — *T., V. I, p. 556.*

CHAPTER XXXV.

PRAYER FOR THE SICK.

1015. It is labor lost to teach people to go to God as a healer of their infirmities, unless they are educated also to lay aside every wrong practise.— *U. T., Aug. 25, 1897*

Cautions. 1016. Many have expected that God would keep them from sickness merely because they have asked him to do so. But God did not regard their prayers, because their faith was not made perfect by works. God will not work a miracle to keep those from sickness who have no care for themselves, but are continually violating the laws of health, and make no effort to prevent disease. When we do all we can on our part to have health, then we may expect that the blessed results will follow, and we can ask God in faith to bless our efforts for the preservation of health. He will then answer our prayer, if his name can be glorified thereby. But let all understand that they have a work to do. God will not work in a miraculous manner to preserve the health of persons who are taking a sure course to make themselves sick, by their careless inattention to the laws of health.— *H. to L., Chap. 4, p. 64.*

1017. In such cases of affliction where Satan has control of the mind, before engaging in prayer there should be the closest self-examination to discover if

there are not sins which need to be repented of, con-
fessed, and forsaken.   Deep humility of soul before
God is necessary, and firm, humble reliance upon
the blood of Christ alone.   Fasting and prayer will
accomplish nothing while the heart is estranged
from God by a wrong course of action.— *T., V. II,
p. 146.*

1018. I had been shown that there was so much
iniquity abounding, even·among professed Sabbath-
keepers, that I did not wish to unite in prayer for
those of whose history I had no knowledge.— *T., V.
II, p. 350.*

1019. What word has God for those who ignore
the light that is shining abroad, and then ask to be
prayed for that they may be sanctified and healed?
— The same word that he had for Cain : "If thou
doest well, shalt thou not be accepted ?   And if thou
doest not well, sin lieth at the door."— *U. T., Aug
25, 1897.*

1020. Some, if they should regain their health, **Instruction.**
would indulge in some heedless transgression of
nature's laws.— *U. T.*

1021. We should first find out if the sick one has
been withholding tithes or has made trouble in the
church.— *U. T.*

1022. There are very many more than we imagine
that are sick mentally. . . . A sore, sick heart, a
discouraged mind, needs mild treatment, and it is
through tender sympathy that this class of minds can
be directed to the Burden-Bearer, and if they can have
faith that he will have an interest in them, the cure

of their diseased bodies and minds will be sure.— *T.*, *V. III, p. 184.*

1023. After the physicians [of the Health Institute] have done what they can in behalf of the sick, they ask God to work with their efforts, and restore the suffering invalids to health. This he has done in some cases in answer to the prayer of faith. And this he will continue to do, if they are faithful, and put their trust in him.— *T., V. II, p. 184.*

1024. God does not work miracles where he has provided means by which the work may be accomplished. —*R. and H., 1888, No. 29.*

1025. Faith without intelligent works is dead, being alone. Faith in the healing power of God will not save unless it is combined with good works.— *U. T., Aug. 25, 1897.*

1026. God will not work a miracle to change natural causes which you can control.— *S. of T., 1884, No. 18.*

1027. Many would not endure the time of trial, and will therefore be laid away.— *U. T.*

1028. Where the way is clear for the offering up of prayer for the sick, the case should be committed to the Lord in calm faith, not with a storm of excitement. He alone is acquainted with the past life of the individual, and knows what his future will be. . . . All that we are required to do is to ask God to raise up the sick if in accordance with his will, believing that he hears the reasons which we present, and the fervent prayers offered. If the Lord sees that it will best honor him, he will answer our prayers. But to urge recovery without submission to his will,

is not right. . . . All that can be done in praying
for the sick is earnestly to importune God in their
behalf, and in perfect confidence rest the matter in
his hands. . . . If the life of the sick can glorify
him, we pray that they may live; nevertheless, not
as we will, but as he wills.   Our faith can be just as
firm, and more reliable, by committing the desire to
the all-wise God, and without feverish anxiety, in perfect confidence, trusting all to him. . . . Our petitions must not take the form of a command, but of
intercession for him to do the thing we desire of him.
— *T., V. II, pp. 147–149.*

1029. The strong desire for recovery leads to
earnest prayer; and this is right.   God is our refuge
in sickness as in health.— *T., No. 32, p. 71.*

1030. Prayer will give the sick an abiding confidence.— *T., No. 32, p. 199.*

1031. Jesus can limit the power of Satan.   He is
the physician in whom the sin-sick soul may trust to
heal the maladies of the body as well as of the soul.
— *T., No. 32, p. 205.*

1032. I would come before the Lord with this
petition: "Lord, we cannot read the heart of this
sick one, but thou knowest whether it is for the good
of his soul and for the glory of thy name to raise him
to health.   In thy great goodness, compassionate
this case, and let healthy action take place in the
system.   The work must be entirely thine own.   We
have done all that human skill can do; now, Lord,
we lay this case at thy feet, work as only God can
work, and if it be for thy good and for thy glory,
arrest the progress of disease and heal this sufferer."

. . . But after I have prayed earnestly for the sick, what then? Do I cease to do all I can for their recovery?— No, I work all the more earnestly, with much prayer that the Lord may bless the means which his own hand has provided; that he may give sanctified wisdom to co-operate with him in the recovery of the sick.— *U. T., March 11, 1892.*

1033. In praying for the sick, it is essential to have faith; for it is in accordance with the word of God. . . . Sometimes answers to our prayers come immediately, sometimes we have to wait patiently and continue earnestly to plead for the things we need. Our faith is illustrated by the case of the importunate solicitor for bread. . . . If our petitions are indited by the Lord, they will be answered.— *Ibid.*

1034. We all desire an immediate answer to our prayers, and we are tempted to become discouraged if it does not come. Now my experience has taught me that this is a great mistake. The delay is for our special benefit. . . . Faith strengthens through continual exercise. This waiting does not mean that because we ask the Lord to heal, there is nothing for us to do. We are to make the very best use of the means which the Lord in his gracious goodness has provided for us in our very necessities. . . . I have looked to God in faith, and have used every benefit that hygienic methods have provided, of which we could avail ourselves. This was my duty. . . . In treatment we have used water in a variety of ways, always asking the Lord to give wisdom in all our efforts, and to put his blessing upon every laudable means employed for the recovery of health. . . . As a reasonable being, through the grace of God I shall take advantage of the blessings of the Lord which he has placed within my reach.— *U. T., March 11, 1892.*

1035. I have seen so much of carrying matters to extremes, even in praying for the sick, that I have felt that this part of our experience requires much earnest, sanctified thinking, else we shall make movements that we may call faith, but that are nothing less than presumption. Persons worn down with affliction need to be counseled wisely that they may move discreetly; and while they place themselves before God to be prayed for that they may be healed, they are not to neglect methods of restoration to health that are in accordance with nature's laws. If, in praying for healing, they refuse to use the simple remedies provided by God to alleviate pain and to aid nature in her work, lest it be a denial of faith, they are taking an unwise position. It is not a denial of faith, it is in strict harmony with the plans of God. . . . One word from God, one touch of the divine finger, would have cured Hezekiah instantly, but special directions were given to take a fig and lay it on the affected part, and Hezekiah was raised to life. In everything we need to move along the line of God's providence. The human agent should have faith, and should co-operate with divine power, using every facility, taking advantage of everything that to his intelligence is beneficial, and working in harmony with natural laws; in doing this he neither denies nor hinders faith.— *Ibid.*

16

1036. Should the Lord work a miracle to restore the wonderful machinery which human beings have impaired through their own carelessness and inattention and their indulgence of appetite and passions, by doing the very things that the Lord has told them they should not do, he would be ministering to sin, which is the transgression of his own law.— *U. T.*, *May 19, 1897.*

1037. The relations between God and each soul are as distinct and full as though there were not another soul for whom he gave his beloved Son. . . . Keep your wants, your joys, your sorrows, your cares, and your fears before God. . . . The Lord is very pitiful and of tender mercy. His heart of love is touched by our sorrows, and even by our utterance of them. . . . Nothing that in any way concerns our peace is too small for him to notice. There is no chapter in our experience too dark for him to read; there is no perplexity too difficult for him to unravel. No calamity can befall the least of his children, no anxiety harass the soul, no joy cheer, no sincere prayer escape the lips, of which our Heavenly Father is unobservant, or in which he takes no immediate interest. "He healeth the broken in heart, and bindeth up their wounds."— *S. to C.*, *p. 117.*

CHAPTER XXXVI.

DRUGS.

1038. Many, instead of seeking to remove the poisonous matter from the system, take a more deadly poison into the system to remove a poison already there.— *H. to L., Chap. 4, p. 64.*

1039. Many parents substitute drugs for judicious nursing.— *H. R.*

1040. Drugs never cure disease; they only change its form and location. . . . When drugs are introduced into the system, for a time they seem to have a beneficial effect. A change may take place, but the disease is not cured. It will manifest itself in some other form. . . . The disease which the drug was given to cure may disappear, but only to reappear in a new form, such as skin diseases, ulcers, painful, diseased joints, and sometimes in a more dangerous and deadly form. . . . Nature keeps struggling, and the patient suffers with different ailments, until there is a sudden breaking down in her efforts, and death follows.— *H. to L., Chap. 3, p. 60.* **Mode of Action.**

1041. Every additional drug given to the patient . . . will complicate the case, and make the patient's recovery more hopeless. . . . An evil, simple in the beginning, which nature aroused herself to overcome, and which she would have done if left to herself, aided by the common blessings of Heaven, has been made tenfold worse by introducing drug poisons into the system, which cause of themselves a destructive disease, forcing into extraordinary action the remaining life forces to war against and overcome the drug intruder.— *H. to L., Chap. 3, p. 57.*

1042. Sick people who take drugs do appear to get well. With some there is sufficient life force for nature to draw upon to so far expel the poison from the system that the sick, having a period of rest, recover. But no credit should be allowed the drugs taken, for they only hindered nature in her efforts. All the credit should be ascribed to nature's restorative powers.— *H. to L., Chap. 3, p. 50.*

1043. Powerful poisons are often administered, which fetter nature in all her friendly efforts to recover from the abuse the system has suffered.— *H. to L., Chap. 3, p. 49.*

Results of Drug Medication.

1044. Drugging should be forever abandoned; for while it does not cure any malady, it enfeebles the system, making it more susceptible to disease.— *T., No. 32, p. 57.*

1045. There are more who die from the use of drugs than all who would have died of disease had nature been left to do her own work.— *H. to L., Chap. 3, p. 61.*

1046. Medicines have no power to cure, but will most generally hinder nature in her efforts.— *H. to L., Chap. 3, p. 62.*

1047. Medicine deranges nature's fine machinery, and breaks down the constitution. It kills, but never cures.— *H. to L., Chap. 3, p. 57.*

1048. The endless variety of medicines in the market, the numerous advertisements of new drugs and mixtures, all of which claim to do wonderful cures, kill hundreds where they benefit one. . . . Yet people keep dosing, and continue to grow weaker until they die. Some will have medicine at all events. Then let them take these hurtful mixtures and the various deadly poisons upon their own responsibility. God's servants should not administer medicines which they know will leave behind injurious effects upon the system, even if they do relieve present suffering. Every poisonous preparation in the vegetable and mineral kingdoms, taken into the system, will leave its wretched influence, affecting the liver and lungs, and deranging the system generally.— *F. of F., p. 140.*

1049. The sick are in a hurry to get well, and the friends of the sick are impatient. They will have medicine, and if they do not feel that powerful influence upon their systems which their erroneous views lead them to think they should feel, they impatiently change to another physician. The change often increases the evil. They go through a course of medicine equally as dangerous as the first, and more fatal, because the two treatments do not agree, and the system is poisoned beyond remedy.— *H. to L., Chap. 3, p. 62.*

1050. Although the patient may recover, yet the powerful effort nature was required to make to overcome the poison, injured the constitution, and shortened the life of the patient. There are many who do not die under the influence of drugs, but there are very many who are left useless wrecks, hopeless, gloomy, and miserable sufferers, a burden to themselves and to society.—*H. to L., Chap. 3, p. 50.*

1051 Everywhere you go you will see deformity, disease, and imbecility, which in very many cases can be traced directly back to drug poisons.— *H. to L., Chap. 3, p. 51.*

1052. Drugs given to stupefy, whatever they may be, derange the nervous system.— *H. to L., Chap. 3, p. 57.*

The Use of Drugs in our Institutions. 1053. Our institutions are established that the sick may be treated by hygienic methods, discarding almost entirely the use of drug**s**. There is a terrible account to be rendered to God by men who have so little regard for human life as to treat the body ruthlessly, in dealing out drugs. . . . We are not excusable if, through ignorance, we destroy God's building by taking into the stomach poisonous drugs under a variety of names we do not understand. It is our duty to refuse all such prescriptions. We want sanitariums where maladies may be cured by nature's own provisions, and where the people may be taught how to treat themselves when sick; where they will learn to eat temperately of wholesome food, and to be educated to discard all narcotics, tea, coffee, fermented wines, and stimulants of all kinds, and the flesh of dead animals.— *U. T., Dec. 4, 1896.*

1054. Drug medication, as it is generally practised, is a curse. Educate away from drugs, use them less and less, and depend more upon hygienic agencies. Nature will respond to God's remedies,— pure air,

pure water, proper exercise, and a clear conscience.
— *U. T.*, *1888.*

1055. To use drugs while continuing evil habits is
certainly inconsistent, and greatly dishonors God by
dishonoring the body which he has made. Yet for
all this, stimulants and drugs continue to be prescribed and freely used; while the hurtful indulgences
that produce the disease are not discarded. The use
of tea, coffee, tobacco, opium, wine, beer, and other
stimulants gives nature a false support. Physicians
should understand how to treat the sick through the
use of nature's remedies. Pure air, pure water, and
healthful exercise should be employed in the treatment of the sick.— *U . T.*, *1892.*

1056. Many physicians are not as thorough and
intelligent as they should be in the practise of their
profession. They resort to drugs, when greater skill
and knowledge would teach them a more excellent
way. Lives have been lost which might have been
saved if drugs had not been resorted to. As a rule,
the less frequently they are employed, the better the
patient will prosper.— *U. T.*, *1888.*

1057. Make use of the remedies that God has provided. Pure air, sunshine, and the intelligent use of
water are beneficial agents in the restoration of
health. But the use of water is considered too
laborious. It is easier to employ drugs than to use
natural remedies.

In treating the sick, the physician will seek God
for wisdom; then, instead of placing his dependence
upon drugs and expecting that medicine will bring
health to his patients, he will use nature's restora-

tives, and employ natural means whereby the sick may be aided to recover. The Lord will hear and answer the prayers of the Christian physician.— *U. T., 1888.*

1058. A great amount of good can be done by enlightening all to whom we have access, as to the best means, not only of curing the sick, but of preventing disease and suffering. The physician who endeavors to enlighten his patients as to the nature and causes of their maladies, and to teach them how to avoid disease, may have up-hill work ; but if he is a conscious reformer, he will talk plainly of the ruinous effects of self-indulgence in eating, drinking, and dressing, of the overtaxation of the vital forces that has brought his patients where they are. He will not increase the evil by administering drugs till exhausted nature gives up the struggle, but will teach the patients how to form correct habits, and to aid nature in her work of restoration by a wise use of her own simple remedies.— *C. T., p. 121.*

1059. The question of health reform is not agitated as it must be and will be. A simple diet and the entire absence of drugs, leaving nature free to recuperate the wasted energies of the body, would make our sanitariums far more effectual in restoring the sick to health.— *U. T., Aug. 30, 1896.*

CHAPTER XXXVII.

THE MISSIONARY NURSE.

1060. In almost every church there are young men and women who might receive an education either as physicians or nurses. They will never have a more favorable opportunity than now. I would urge that this subject be considered prayerfully, that special effort be made to select those youth who give promise of usefulness and moral strength. Let these receive an education at our Sanitarium at Battle Creek, to go out as missionaries wherever the Lord may call them to labor.— *M. M., V. II, p. 216.* **Need of Nurses.**

1061. I could wish that there were one hundred nurses in training where there is one. It ought to be thus. Both men and women can be much more useful as medical missionaries than as missionaries without a medical education.— *M. M., V. II, p. 215.*

1062. Attendants should be cheerful and hopeful. — *H. to L., Chap. 3, p. 54.* **Qualifications of Nurses.**

1063. The attendants should be unhurried, calm, and self-possessed.— *H. to L., Chap. 4, p. 59.*

1064. The mother may be an intelligent nurse and physician of her own dear children. It is her right to have an understanding of her own and her children's organisms, that she may know how to treat her children in sickness.— *H. R.*

1065. It is the duty of attendants and nurses in the sick-room to have a special care for their own health, especially in critical cases of fever and consumption. One person should not be kept closely confined to the sick-room. It is safer to have two or three to depend upon, who are careful and understanding nurses, these alternating and sharing the care and confinement of the sick-room. Each should have exercise in the open air as often as possible. This is important to sick-bed attendants, especially if the friends of the sick are among that class who continue to regard air, if admitted into the sick-room, as an enemy, and will not allow the windows raised or the doors opened. The sick and the attendants are in this case compelled to breathe the atmosphere from day to day, because of the inexcusable ignorance of the friends of the sick.— *H. to L., Chap. 4, p. 56.*

1066. If attendants are awake to the subject of health, and realize the necessity of ventilation for their own benefit, as well as that of the patient, and the relatives, as well as the sick, oppose the admission of air and light into the sick-room, the attendants should have no scruples of conscience in leaving the sick-room. They should feel themselves released from their obligations to the sick. It is not the duty of one or more to risk the liability of incurring disease and endangering their lives by breathing the poisonous atmosphere. If the sick will fall victims to their own erroneous ideas, and will shut out of the room the most essential of heaven's blessings, let them do so, but not at the peril of those who ought to live.— *H. to L., Chap. 4, p. 57.*

1067. It is of great value to the sick to have an even temperature in the room. This cannot always be correctly determined, if left to the judgment of attendants, for they may not be the best judges of a right temperature.— *H. to L., Chap. 4, p. 54.* **Suggestions to Nurses.**

1068. Few realize the effect of a mild, firm manner, even in the care of an infant. The fretful, impatient mother or nurse creates feverishness in the child in her arms, whereas a gentle manner tends to quiet the nerves of the little one.— *H. R.*

1069. Where there are two watchers, they often converse together, sometimes aloud, but more frequently in whispered tones, which is far more trying and exciting to the nerves of the sick than talking aloud. . . . Attendants upon the sick should, if possible, leave them to quiet and rest through the night, while they occupy a room adjoining. All unnecessary noise and excitement should be avoided in the sick-room, and the whole house should be kept as quiet as possible. Ignorance, forgetfulness, and recklessness have caused the death of many who might have lived had they received proper care from judicious, thoughtful attendants.— *H. to L., Chap. 4, p. 59.*

CHAPTER XXXVIII.

MEDICAL STUDENTS.

1070. I am intensely interested in the education of medical students as missionaries. This will prove a means of introducing the truth where otherwise it would not find an entrance.— *U. T.*, *Oct. 2, 1895.*

1071. I can see that in the Lord's providence the medical missionary work is to be a great entering wedge, whereby the diseased soul may be reached.— *Ibid.*

1072. What a field of usefulness is open before the medical missionary! Jesus Christ was in every sense of the word a missionary of the highest type, combining with his missionary work that of the great Physician, healing all manner of diseases. . . . Every physician ought to be a Christian, and if he is, he bears with him a cure for the soul as well as the body. He is doing the work of an apostle as well as of a physician. . . . How essential that the missionary should understand the diseases which afflict the human body, that he may combine the physician, trained to care for diseased bodies, with the faithful, conscientious shepherd of the flock, giving sacredness and double efficiency to the service! The Lord, in his great goodness and matchless love, has been urging it upon his human instrumentalities that the education of missionaries

[252]

is not really complete unless they have a knowledge of how to treat the sick and suffering. If the importance of this branch of missionary education had been felt, many who have lost their lives might have lived. Had they had an intelligent knowledge of the human body and how to treat its maladies, they could have reached many darkened minds that have not been reached.— *Ibid.*

1073. Devout persons, both men and women, are wanted now to go forth as medical missionaries. Let them cultivate their physical and mental powers and their piety to the utmost. Every effort should be made to send forth intelligent workers. The same grace that came from Jesus Christ to Paul and Apollos, which caused them to be distinguished for their spiritual excellencies, can be received now, and will bring into working order many devoted missionaries.— *U. T., Feb. 19, 1893.*

1074. I consider that there is nothing that can give character to the work like a proper taking up of the work of hygienic treatment for the sick.— *U. T., Feb. 10, 1897.*

1075. As religious aggression subverts the liberties of our nation, those who would stand for freedom of conscience will be placed in unfavorable positions. For their own sake they should, while they have opportunity, become intelligent in regard to disease, its causes, prevention, and cure. Those who do this will find a field of labor anywhere. There will be suffering ones, plenty of them, who will need help, not only among those of our own faith, but largely among those who know not the truth.— *S. T., Sept. 16, 1892.*

1076. I would advise young men and women to give heed to this matter. Perilous times are before us. The whole world will be involved in perplexity and distress. Diseases of every kind will be upon the human family, and such ignorance as now prevails concerning the laws of health will result in great suffering and the loss of many lives that might be saved.— *S. T., Sept. 16, 1893.*

1077. There is no missionary field more important than that occupied by the faithful, God-fearing physician. There is no field where a man may accomplish greater good, or win more jewels to shine in the crown of his rejoicing.— *T., No. 32, p. 204.*

1078. More of the right kind of men are needed to devote themselves to this profession.— *T., No. 32, p. 202.*

Qualifications of Medical Students. 1079. A physician can do much better work if he has physical strength. If he is feeble, he cannot endure the wearing labor incident to his calling. A man who has a weak constitution, who is a dyspeptic, or who has not perfect self-control, cannot become qualified to deal with all classes of disease. Great care should be taken not to encourage persons who might be useful in some less responsible position, to study medicine at a great outlay of time and means, when there is no reasonable hope that they will succeed.— *T., No. 32, p. 203.*

1080. Painstaking effort should be made to induce suitable men to qualify themselves for this work. They should be men whose characters are based upon the broad principles of the word of God, men who possess a natural energy, force, and perseverance that will enable them to reach a high standard of excellence. It is not every one who can make a successful physician. Many have entered upon the duties of this profession every way unprepared. They have not the requisite knowledge; neither have they the skill and tact, the carefulness and intelligence, necessary to insure success.— *T., No. 32, p. 202.*

1081. Those who take the lives of others in their hands must be men who have been marked as making life a success. They must be men of judgment and wisdom, men who can sympathize, and feel to the depths, men whose whole being is stirred when they witness suffering.— *T., V. II, p. 385.*

1082. There are those who have entered the medical profession who should have chosen some other calling. They are unsympathetic. They seem to think the proper way is to withhold all words of sympathy, and gird up their compassion so that not a particle of it shall be drawn out. They are cold and uncommunicative, and leave no warm, cheering influence. They seem to think words of tenderness and compassion are an evidence of weakness.— *Counsel to Physicians and Medical Students, p. 28.*

1083. God will surely advance the humble, faithful, praying, whole-souled medical missionary, as he advanced Daniel and his fellows.— *S. T., Oct. 2, 1893.*

1084. The duties and qualifications of a physician **are not small.** The students need daily to lift re-

sponsibilities, that they may become burden-bearers.
. . . There is only one power that can make these
students what they ought to be, and keep them stead-
fast.   It is the grace of God and the power of the
truth exerting a saving influence upon the life and
character.   These students, who intend to deal with
suffering humanity, will find no graduating place this
side of heaven.   Every bit possible of that knowledge
that is termed science should be acquired, while the
seeker daily acknowledges that the fear of God is the
beginning of wisdom.   Every item of experience and
everything that can strengthen the mind, should be
cultivated to the utmost of their power, while at the
same time they should seek God for his wisdom, their
consciences illuminated, quick, and pure; for unless
they are guided by the wisdom from above, they
become an easy prey to the deceptive power of
Satan.   They become inflated, large in their own
eyes, pompous, and self-sufficient.   The principle of
worldly policy will most assuredly lead into difficulties.   The truth, God's truth, must be cherished in
the heart, and held in the strength of God, or the
powers of Satan will wrench it from you.   You need
to be self-reliant and yet teachable, that you may
have strength to be faithful to duty.   To trust to
your own resources, your own wisdom or strength,
is folly.   You will be brought to confusion if you do
this.   You can walk securely only when you follow
the counsel of God.— *Counsel to Physicians and Medical Students, p. 17.*

1085.   Knowledge and science must be vitalized by
the Spirit of God in order to serve the noblest pur-

poses.   The Christian alone can make the right use
of knowledge.   Science, in order to be fully appreciated, must be viewed from a religious standpoint.
— *C. E., p. 32.*

1086. I wish I could set before the medical stu-   Advice to
Medical
Students.
dent the true responsibility that rests upon him and
his work.   There is not one in one hundred who has a
just sense of his position, his work, his accountability
to God, and how much God will do for him if he
will make him his trust. ˙ The very first lesson he
should learn is that of dependence upon God.   Make
God your counselor at every step.   The worldly and
the nominal Christian may insinuate that in order to
be successful you must be politic, you must at times
depart from the strictest rectitude; but be not de-
luded.   These temptations find a ready welcome in
the heart of man; but I speak that which I know.
Pamper not self.   Throw not open a door for the
enemy to take possession of the citadel of the soul.
There is danger in the first and slightest departure from
the strictest veracity.   In your work, be true to yourself.   Preserve your God-given dignity in the fear of
God.   There is in your case the necessity of getting
hold and keeping hold of the arm of infinite power.
— *Counsel to Physicians and Medical Students, p. 23.*

1087. By studying the word of God diligently
medical students are far better prepared for all other
studies; for enlightenment always comes with an
earnest study of the word of God.   Let it be understood by medical missionaries that the better they
become acquainted with God and Jesus Christ whom
he has sent, the better they become acquainted with

Bible history, the better qualified they will be to do their work. . . . There should be most faithful teachers who strive to make the students understand their lessons, not by explaining everything themselves, but by letting the students explain thoroughly every passage which they read. Let the inquiring minds of the students be respected.—*U. T.*, *Dec. 1, 1895.*

1088. Learn all they can of the principles of truth, and discard error.— *C. E., p. 38.*

1089. In this age there is danger for every one who shall enter upon the study of medicine. Often his instructors are world-wise men, and his fellow students infidels, who have no thought of God, and he is in danger of being influenced by these irreligious associations. Nevertheless, some have gone through the medical course, and have remained true to principle. They would not continue their studies on the Sabbath; and they have proved that men may become qualified for the duties of a physician, and not disappoint the expectations of those who furnish them means to obtain an education.— *T., No. 32, p. 203.*

1090. Students may receive their diplomas, and yet their education be but just begun. . . . The one who best knows himself works in all humility. He feels like making no proud boasts ; he bears a weight cf responsibility as he sees the woes of suffering humanity, and he will not take human life into his hand to deal with even the bodies of men without connecting with the experienced Physician, regarding him as a father and himself as a child to be instructed and corrected, if in error. . . . Students should work up an experience beginning at the lower round of the ladder, and by careful, earnest, thoughtful exertion, climb round after round, religion, Bible religion, being the mainspring of action. They cannot expect to be ranked by the side of those of experience who have devoted their time, their energies, and their souls to the work for years, unless they shall give evidence of capabilities of mind and intelligence in practise. . . . They must be content to come up gradually, and prove their ability by showing in lesser matters that they sense the responsibility laid upon them. Many do not love the taxing, burden-bearing part. They will deal with the sick, but never lift the load. They take every thing very easily. The sick may approach the last crisis that wrings the heart of the older physician with intense pain because a life is going out and he can devise no means of saving it, and another physician connected with him will not sense the danger or devote time to close thought and severe mental effort. He works as a machine. He is as calm as a summer's evening, when he should be pressed as a cart beneath the sheaves. Had he more intensity of feeling, he would not throw off the burden for an instant, but by close thinking, by earnest prayer, would study to devise ways and means yet untried, and would perhaps be able to save not only the life, but, through Christ, the soul of the patient.— *Counsel to Physicians and Medical Students, pp. 11–13.*

1091. Students should be willing to work under those of experience, to heed their suggestions, to follow their advice, and to go as far as possible in thought, training, and intelligent enterprise, but never to infringe upon a rule, never to disregard one principle that has been interwoven in the upbuilding of the institution. The dropping down is easy enough; the disregard of regulations is natural to the heart inclined to selfish ease and gratification. It is so much easier to tear down than to build up. One man with careless ideas may do more in this work of letting down the standard than ten men with all their efforts can do to counteract and stay the demoralizing influence. . . .

There are many who are in such haste to climb to distinction that they skip some of the rounds of the ladder, and have, in so doing, lost essential experience, which they should have in order to become intelligent workers. In their zeal the knowledge of many things looks unimportant to them. They skim over the surface, and do not go deep and thorough, climbing round after round of the ladder of progress by a slow and painful process, thus gaining an experience which will enable them to help others to ascend. We want men and women who are more thorough, and who feel it their duty to improve every talent lent them, that they may finally double their intrusted capital.— *Ibid., p. 15.*

1092. A responsibility to spread the knowledge of hygienic principles rests upon all who have enjoyed the benefits of health reform. . . . There must be a revival in regard to this matter; for God purposes to accomplish much through this agency.— *S. T.*

CHAPTER XXXIX.

THE MISSIONARY PHYSICIAN.

1093. The duties of the physician are arduous. Few realize the mental and physical strain to which he is subjected. Every energy and capability must be enlisted with the most intense anxiety in the battle with disease and death. Often he knows that one unskilful movement of the hand, even but a hair's breadth, in the wrong direction may send a soul unprepared into eternity.— *T., No. 32, p. 202.*

1094. The physician who endeavors to enlighten his patients as to the nature and causes of their maladies, and to teach them how to avoid disease, may have up-hill work.— *C. T., p. 121.*

1095. Why should the Christian physician, who is believing, expecting, looking, waiting, and longing for the coming and kingdom of Christ, when sickness and death will no longer have power over the saints, expect more pay for his services than the Christian editor or the Christian minister? He may say that his work is more wearing. That is yet to be proved. Let him work as he can endure it, and not violate the laws of life which he teaches to his patients. There are no good reasons why he should overwork and receive large pay for it, more than the minister or the editor. Let all who act a part in the institute and receive pay for their services, act on the same liberal principle.— *T.*, *V. I, p. 640.*

1096. The physicians should keep well. They must not get sick by overlabor, or by any imprudence on their part. . . . The privilege of getting away from the Health Institute should occasionally be accorded to all the physicians, especially to those who bear burdens of responsibilities. If there is such a scarcity of help that this cannot be done, more help should be secured. To have physicians overworked, and thus disqualified to perform the duties of their profession, is a thing to be dreaded.— *T., V. III, p. 182.*

Christian Physicians.

1097. Satan is the originator of disease; and the physician is warring against his work and power.— *T., No. 32, p. 200.*

1098. Every energy and capability must be enlisted with the most intense anxiety in the battle with disease and death.— *Ibid., p. 202.*

1099. He will be firm as a rock as to principle, yet kind and courteous to all. He will feel the responsibility of his position, and his practise will show that he is actuated by pure, unselfish motives, and a desire to adorn the doctrine of Christ in all things.— *Ibid., p. 195.*

1100. The physician should know how to pray.— *Ibid., p. 199.*

1101. Both the health of the body and the salvation of the soul are in a degree dependent upon the course of the physicians. It is of the utmost consequence that they be right, that they have not only scientific knowledge, but the knowledge of God's will and ways.— *T.*, *V. IV, p. 566.*

1102. The young physician has access to the God of Daniel. Through divine grace and power, he may become as efficient in his calling as Daniel was in his exalted position. But it is a mistake to make a scientific preparation the all-important thing, while religious principles that lie at the very foundation of a successful practise are neglected Many are lauded as skilful men in their profession, who scorn the thought that they need to rely upon Jesus for wisdom in their work. But if these men who trust in their knowledge of science were illuminated by the light of heaven, to how much greater excellence might they attain ! How much stronger would be their powers, with how much greater confidence could they undertake difficult cases ! The man who is closely connected with the great Physician of soul and body, has the resources of heaven and earth at his command, and he can work with a wisdom, an unerring precision, that the godless man cannot possess.— *T., No. 32, p. 204.*

1103. The physician needs more than human wisdom and power that he may know how to minister to the many perplexing cases of disease of the mind and heart with which he is called to deal. If he is ignorant of the power of divine grace, he cannot help the afflicted one, but may aggravate the difficulty; but if he has a firm hold upon God, he will be able to help the diseased, distracted mind.— *Ibid.,* *p. 200.*

1104. If he takes counsel of God, he will have the great Healer to work with his efforts, and he will move with the greatest caution, lest by his mismanagement he injure one of God's creatures.— *Ibid., p. 195.*

Scientific Attainments of Physicians. 1105. Many have entered upon the duties of this profession every way unprepared. They have not the requisite knowledge ; neither have they the skill and tact, the carefulness and intelligence, necessary to insure success.— *T., No. 32, p. 2.*

1106. Many physicians are not as thorough and intelligent as they ought to be in the practise of their profession. They resort to drugs, when greater skill and knowledge would teach them a more excellent way.— *U. T., 1888.*

1107. When physicians understand physiology in its truest sense, their use of drugs will be very much less, and finally they will cease to use them at all. The physician who depends upon drug medication in his practise shows that he does not understand the delicate machinery of the human organism.—*U. T., Oct. 12, 1896.*

1108. A skilful physician must understand the nature of various diseases, and must have a thorough knowledge of the human structure. He must be prompt in attending to the patients. He knows that delays are dangerous. When his experienced hand is laid upon the pulse of the sufferer, and he carefully notes the peculiar indications of the malady, his previous knowledge enables him to determine concerning the nature of the disease and the treatment necessary to arrest its progress.— *T., V. IV, p. 267.*

1109. If he is an intelligent physician, he will be able to trace disease to its cause.— *T., No. 32, p 196.*

1110. If he will be observing and honest, he cannot help acknowledging that sin and disease bear to each other the relationship of cause and effect. The physician should be quick to see this, and to act accordingly.— *Ibid., p. 200.*

1111. There are constant temptations for physicians to exalt science above the God who is the ruler of the universe. There is danger that physicians will, little by little, leave the simplicity of Bible faith in the power of God.— *U. T., April 15, 1892.*

1112. All who engage in the acquisition of knowledge should aim to reach the highest round of progress. Let them advance as fast and as far as they can; let their field of study be as broad as their powers can compass, making God their wisdom; clinging to him who is infinite in knowledge, who can reveal the secrets hidden for ages, who can solve the most difficult problems for minds that believe in him who only hath immortality, dwelling in the light that no man can approach unto. . . . The same principles run through the spiritual and the natural worlds.— *S. T. on E., p. 216.*

1113. It is wilful sin in them to be ignorant of the laws of health or indifferent to them; for they are looked up to as wise above other men.— *T., No. 32, p. 197.*

The Physician's Relation to the Laws of Health

1114. If they do not put to a practical use the knowledge they have of the laws that govern their own being, if they prefer present gratification to soundness of mind and body, they are not fit to be intrusted with the lives of others.— *Ibid.*, *p. 198.*

1115. He [the physician] is expected to indulge in no habit that will weaken the life forces.— *Ibid.*, *p. 197.*

1116. The physicians in our institutions must be imbued with the living principles of health reform. Men will never be truly temperate until the grace of Christ is an abiding principle in the heart.— *U. T.*, *Oct. 12, 1896.*

1117. Men are wanted at the Institute who will have the fear of God before them, who can minister to sick minds, and keep prominent the health reform from a religious standpoint.— *T., V. III, p. 168.*

1118. If a man who assumes so grave a responsibility as that of a physician, sins against himself in not conforming to nature's laws, he will reap the consequences of his own doings, and abide her righteous decision, from which there can be no appeal. . . . His capabilities for doing good are lessened. He will lead others in the path his own feet are traveling. Hundreds will follow the example of one intemperate physician, feeling that they are safe in doing what the doctor does. And in the day of God he will meet the record of his own course, and be called to give an account for all the good he might have done, but did not do, because by his own voluntary act he weakened his physical and mental powers by selfish indulgence.— *T.*, *No. 32, p. 198.*

The Physician's Relation to His Patients. 1119. He will not look upon his patient as a mere piece of human mechanism, but as a soul to be saved or lost.— *T.*, *No. 32, p. 202.*

1120. Unless the physicians can obtain the confidence of their patients, they can never help them.—
T., V. III, p. 79.

1121. Never should a physician neglect his patients.— *U. T.*

1122. The work of the Christian physician does not end with healing the maladies of the body; his efforts should extend to the diseases of the mind, to the saving of the soul. It may not be his duty, unless asked, to present any theoretical points of truth; but he may point his patients to Christ. The lessons of the divine Teacher are ever appropriate. He should call the attention of the repining to the ever fresh tokens of the love and care of God, to his wisdom and goodness as manifested in his created works. The mind can then be led through nature up to nature's God, and centered on the heaven which he has prepared for those who love him.—
T., No. 32, p. 199.

1123. Physicians who would be successful in the treatment of disease should know how to minister to a diseased mind.— *T., V. III, p. 169.*

1124. It should be the work of the God-fearing physician to guide the mind of patients to right principles. If patients are left to their own natural bias, they will indulge appetite, because it is a habit, at the expense of health and life. . . . True, their appetite craves unwholesome articles of food, and the disuse of these things will be felt strongly. But the only right course to be pursued in these cases is to educate the conscience, to lay before the patients the effect of these things upon the physical and mental powers to weaken the constitution and induce disease.— *U. T., Feb. 1, 1888.*

1125. Let your influence be persuasive, binding people to your heart because you love Jesus, and because these precious souls are his purchased possession. This is a great work. If, by your Christ-like words and actions, you make impressions that will kindle in their hearts a hungering and thirsting after righteousness and truth, you are a co-laborer with Christ. . . . Enlighten their minds by means of talks and lectures, in regard to the effects of tea, coffee, and flesh meats, and thus lead them to a voluntary correction of their habits.— *Ibid.*

1126. When he has gained the confidence of the afflicted by relieving their sufferings and bringing them back from the verge of the grave, he may teach them that disease is the result of sin; and that it is the fallen foe who seeks to allure them to health-and-soul-destroying practises. He may impress their minds with the necessity of denying self, and obeying the laws of life and health. In the minds of the young especially he may instil right principles.— *T., No. 32, p. 200.*

1127. It seldom does any good to talk in a censuring manner to patients who are diseased in body and mind. But few who have moved in the society of the world, and who view things from the worldling's standpoint, are prepared to have a statement of facts in regard to themselves presented before them. The truth even is not to be spoken at all times. There is a fit time and opportunity to speak, when words will not offend.— *T., V. III, p. 182.*

1128. The physician should be a strictly temperate man. . . . He knows that much of the suffering he seeks to relieve is the result of intemperance and other forms of selfish indulgence. He is called to attend young men, and men in the prime of life and in mature age, who have brought disease upon themselves by the use of tobacco. If he is an intelligent physician, he will be able to trace disease to its cause; but unless he is free from the use of tobacco himself, he will hesitate to put his finger upon the plague-spot, and faithfully unfold to his patients the *cause* of their sickness. He will fail to urge upon the young the necessity of overcoming the habit before it becomes fixed. . . . If he uses the weed himself, how can he present to the inexperienced youth its injurious effects, not only upon themselves, but upon those around them? — *T., No. 32, p. 195.*

1129. How can he place the feet of others on the ladder of progress, while he himself is treading the downward way? — *Ibid., p. 197.*

1130. The practising physician will instruct those who do not understand how to preserve the strength and health they already have, and how to prevent disease by a wise use of heaven's remedies, — pure water, air, and diet. — *T., V. I, p. 490.*

1131. If he does the work enjoined upon him by the Ruler of the universe, he will protest against iniquity in every form and in every degree; he will exert his authority and influence on the side of self-denial and strict, undeviating obedience to the just requirements of God. — *T., No. 32, p. 197.*

The Physician's Relation to Society.

1132. Such a physician will possess a heaven-born
dignity, and will be a powerful agent for good in
the world. Although he may not be appreciated
by those who have no connection with God, yet he
will be honored of Heaven.   In God's sight he will
be more precious than gold, even the gold of Ophir.
— *Ibid.*

1133. If you are a Christian and a competent
physician, you are qualified to do tenfold more
good as a missionary for God than if you were to
go forth merely as a preacher of the word.— *M. M.,
V. II, p. 216.*

1134. While brought in contact with the world,
you should be on your guard that you do not seek
too ardently for the applause of men, and live for
their opinion.— *T., V. IV, p. 568.*

CHAPTER XL.

MEDICAL MISSIONARY WORK.

1135. The prosperity of the medical missionary The Present Need. work is in God's order. This work must be done; the truth must be carried to the highways and hedges. — *S. T., No. 10.*

1136. Why has it not been understood from the word of God that the work being done in medical missionary lines is a fulfilment of the scriptures? "Go out quickly into the streets and lanes of the city, and bring hither the poor, and the maimed, and the halt, and the blind. . . . Go out into the highways and hedges and compel them to come in, that my house may be filled." — *R. and H., 1897, No. 21.*

1137. The educational work in medical missionary lines is a great advance step toward awakening man to a sense of his moral responsibilities. — *U. T., Jan. 11, 1897.*

1138. As religious aggression subverts the liberties of our nation, those who would stand for freedom of conscience will be placed in unfavorable positions. For their own sakes they should, while they have opportunity, become intelligent in regard to disease, its causes, prevention, and cure. Those who do this will find a field of labor anywhere. There will be suffering ones, plenty of them, who will need help, not only among those of our own faith, but largely among those who know not the truth.— *M. M., V. II, p. 216.*

Aim to Educate.

1139. They need an education in the science of how to treat the sick, for this will give them a welcome in any place.— *U. T., Dec. 20, 1896.*

1140. If we would elevate the moral standard of any country where we may be called to go, we must begin by correcting the physical habits of the people. — *M. M., V. II, p. 216.*

1141. The Lord has given special light concerning our hygienic principles, which should be given to others. . . . Those who are in ignorance are to be educated how to live in accordance with pure principles ; to practise those things that will preserve the body in a healthy condition.— *U. T., July 5, 1892.*

1142. The medical missionary can do a great amount of good by educating the people as to how to live.— *R. and H., 1895, No. 25.*

1143. Rally workers who possess true missionary zeal, and let them go forth to diffuse light and knowledge far and near. Let them take the living principles of health reform into communities that to a large degree are ignorant of how they should live.— *U. T., July, 1895.*

Open Fields.

1144. The South is a field where medical missionary work can be one of the greatest blessings.— *S. T., No. 6, p. 49.*

1145. Those who love Christ will do the works of Christ. They will go forth to seek and to save that which was lost. They will not shun those who are despised, and turn aside from the colored race.

They will teach them how to read and how to perform manual labor, educating them to till the soil and to follow trades of various kinds. . . . The work pointed out is a most needful missionary enterprise.— *R. and H., 1896, No. 2.*

1146. The field for medical missionary work is open before us. We are now beginning to comprehend the light given years ago,— that health reform principles would form an entering wedge to the introduction of religious principles. To voice the words of John, "Behold the Lamb of God that taketh away the sins of the world." Would that all our workers might be enlightened, so that they could work intelligently as medical missionaries, for such knowledge would serve as credentials to them in finding access to homes and families wherein to sow the seeds of truth. We want to feel as Christ felt,— that we cannot abandon helpless, suffering ones to the evils of orphanage, and ignorance, and want, and sin, and crime.— *U. T., June 13, 1895.*

CHAPTER XLI.

CHRISTIAN HELP WORK.

Christ's Ambassadors. 1147. This is the special work now before us.— *T., V. II, p. 34.*

1148. Our own human affections and sympathies are not to wane away and become extinct, but through living connection with God our love is to deepen, our interest to become more intense, our efforts more successful in promoting the happiness of those around us. . . . Souls about us are perishing for sympathy which is never expressed.— *S. of T., 1893, No. 34.*

1149. The Lord has set before you another work, the work of extending the truth by establishing centers of interest in cities, and sending workers into the highways and hedges.— *S. T., No. 10, p. 6.*

1150. Many individuals might be laboring in towns and cities, visiting from house to house, becoming acquainted with families, entering into their social life, dining at their tables, entering into conversation by their firesides, dropping the precious seed of truth all along the line. As they exercise their talents, Christ will give them wisdom, and many believers will be found rejoicing in the knowledge of the truth as a result of their labors.— *R. and H., 1895, No. 28.*

1151. The standard of truth may be raised by humble men and women, and the youth, and even children, may be a blessing to others, by revealing what the truth has done for them. God will use the most feeble instruments if they are wholly submitted to him. He can work through them to reach souls to whom the minister could not obtain access. There are the highways and byways to be searched. With your Bible in your hand, with your heart warm and glowing with the love of God, you may go out and tell others your experience; you may make known to them the truth that has impressed your heart, praying with faith that God will make your efforts successful in their salvation. Communicate light, and you will have more light to communicate. Thus you may become laborers together with God. —*R. and H., 1897, No. 2.*

1152. No verbal description could reveal God to the world. Our Saviour employed human faculties, for only by adopting these could he be comprehended by humanity. Only humanity could reach humanity. He lived out the character of God through the human body which God had prepared for him. . . . If our people would administer to other souls who need their help, they would themselves be ministered unto by the chief Shepherd, and thousands would be rejoicing in the fold who are now wandering in the desert. Let every soul go to work to seek and to save the lost, . . . visiting the dark places of the earth where there are no churches.—*R. and H., 1895, No. 26.*

1153. In the path which the poor, the neglected, the suffering, and the sorrowing must tread, Christ walked while on earth, taking upon him all the woes

which the afflicted must bear.   His home was among
the poor.   His family was not distinguished by
learning, riches, or position.   For many years he
worked at his trade as a carpenter.— *Instruction to
R. and H., May 26, 1896.*

1154. Union with Christ means the dispensing of
his blessings.— *S. of T., 1895, No. 37.*

1155. The angels look upon the distressed of
God's family upon the earth, and they are prepared
to co-operate with the human agent in relieving oppression and suffering.   They will co-operate with
those who "break every yoke," who "bring the
poor that are cast out to thy house."— *R. and H.,
1895, No. 1.*

**Our Duty to
the Poor.**
1156. There is no case of need for which some
one is not responsible.— *S. of T., 1895, No. 32.*

1157. As long as there are hungry ones in God's
world to be fed, naked ones to be clothed, souls perishing for the bread and water of salvation, every
unnecessary indulgence, every overplus of capital,
pleads for the poor and needy.

1158. The poor and the needy were objects of his
[Christ's] special attention.   He sought to inspire
with hope the most rough and unpromising, setting
before them the idea that they might become blame-
less and harmless, attaining such a character as
would make them manifest as the children of God
among a crooked and perverse generation, among
whom they would shine as lights in the world.—
S. of T., 1896, No. 31.

1159. What sacrifice are we ready to make that we
may find the lost pearl, and place it in the hands of

our Saviour ?   The cities are teeming with iniquity;
Satan suggests that it is impossible to do any good
within their borders, and so they are sadly neglected.
But there are lost pearls there, whose value you cannot realize until you earnestly seek to find them
There might be one hundred workers where there is
but one seeking diligently, prayerfully, and with intense interest to find the pearls that are buried in the
rubbish of these cities.—*R. and H., 1896, No. 16.*

1160. When heavenly intelligences see those who
claim to be sons and daughters of God putting forth
Christlike efforts to help the erring, manifesting a
tender, sympathetic spirit for the repentant and the
fallen, angels press close to them, and bring to their
remembrance the very words that will soothe and up-
lift the soul. . . . Jesus has given his precious life,
his personal attention, to the least of God's little
ones ; and the angels that excel in strength encamp
round about them that fear God.   Then let us be
on our guard, and never permit one contemptuous
thought to occupy the mind in regard to one of
the little ones of God.   We should look after the
erring with solicitude, and speak encouraging words
to the fallen, and fear lest by some unwise action we shall turn them away from the pitying
Saviour. . . . There is a large, a very large number of straying and lost sheep that have perished in
the wild deserts of sin, simply because no one went
after them to search for them and to bring them back
to the fold.   Jesus uses the illustration of a lost
sheep to show the need of seeking after those who
have wandered from him; for a sheep once lost will

never find its way back to the fold without help.   It
must be sought for, it must be carried back to the
fold.— *R. and H., 1896, No. 26.*

1161. We shall find the footprints of Jesus by the
sick-bed, by the side of suffering humanity, in the
hovels of the poverty stricken and distressed.   We
may walk in these footsteps, comforting the suffering, speaking words of hope and comfort to the de-
spondent.   Doing as Jesus did when he was upon
earth, we shall walk in his blessed steps.— *R. and
H., 1896, No. 23.*

1162. When the sick and wretched applied to the
Saviour for help, he first relieved the poor, suffering
body before he attempted to administer to the darkened mind.   When the present misery of the sup-
plicant was removed, his thoughts could better be
directed into the channel of light and truth.— *S. of
T., 1889, No. 2.*

1163. When he sent out his disciples, he commis-
sioned them to heal the sick as well as to preach the
gospel.   When he sent forth the seventy, he com-
manded them to heal the sick, and next to preach that
the kingdom of God had come nigh unto them.
Their physical health was to be first cared for, in
order that the way might be prepared for their minds
to be reached by those truths which the apostles were
to preach.   The Saviour of the world devoted more
time and labor to healing the afflicted of their maladies than to preaching.   His last injunction to his
apostles, his representatives upon the earth, was to
lay hands on the sick that they might recover.   When
the Master shall come, he will commend those who

have visited the sick and relieved the necessities of the afflicted.— *T., V. IV, p. 225.*

1164. There are multitudes of poor children who need care and protection. There are multitudes of aged people who are dependent upon others for the necessities of life. The Lord has not designed that these sufferers should be neglected.— *R. and H., 1896, No. 11.* **Our Duty to Orphans and the Aged.**

1165. Let the condition of helpless little ones appeal to every mother's heart, that she may put into exercise a mother's love for homeless orphan children. Their helplessness appeals to every God-given attribute in human nature.— *M. M., V. IV, p. 321.*

1166. Do we expect that those who are lost will be faultless? If you would do something to be approved of Heaven, take a child who needs help, who needs forbearance, and the grace of Christ. We choose associates because we think they will benefit us; but Christ sought association with those whom he could benefit.— *S. of T., 1889, No 13.*

1167. Our happiness will be proportionate to our unselfish works, prompted by divine love; for in the plan of salvation God has appointed the law of action and reaction, making the work of beneficence in all its branches twice blessed.— *S. of T., 1886, No. 45.* **Blessing to Christian Helpers.**

1168. No one can give place in his own heart and life for the stream of God's blessing to flow to others, without receiving in himself a rich reward.— *M. of B., p. 112.*

CHAPTER XLII.

LESSONS FROM THE EXPERIENCE OF THE CHILDREN OF ISRAEL.

The Modern Church Repeating the History of Ancient Israel.

1169. The trials of the children of Israel, and their attitude just before the first coming of Christ, have been presented before me again and again to illustrate the position of the people of God in their experience before the second coming of Christ.— *R. and H., 1890, No. 7.*

1170. Satan's snares are laid for us as verily as they were laid for the children of Israel just prior to their entrance into the land of Canaan. We are repeating the history of that people.— *T., No. 31, p. 156.*

1171. I have seen that self-glorification was becoming common among Seventh-day Adventists, and that unless the pride of man should be abased and Christ exalted, we should, as a people, be in no better condition to receive Christ at his second advent than the Jewish people were to receive him at his first advent . . . Their history should be a solemn warning to us.— *T., No. 33, p. 256.*

1172. "I call heaven and earth to record this day against you, that I have set before you life and death, blessing and cursing; therefore choose life, that both thou and thy seed may live; that thou

mayest love the Lord thy God, and that thou mayest
obey his voice, and that thou mayest cleave unto
him; for he is thy life, and the length of thy days;
that thou mayest dwell in the land which the Lord
sware unto thy fathers, to Abraham, to Isaac, and to
Jacob, to give them."

This song was not historical but prophetic. While
it recounted the wonderful dealings of God with his
people in the past, it. also foreshadowed the great
events of the future, the final victory of the faithful
when Christ shall come the second time in power and
glory.— *P. P., p. 467.*

1173. The apostle Paul plainly states that the experience of the Israelites in their travels has been recorded for the benefit of those living in this age of
the world, those upon whom the ends of the world
are come. We do not consider that our dangers are
any less than those of the Hebrews, but greater.—
T., V. III, p. 358.

1174. God in mercy called them out from the
Egyptians, that they might worship him without hindrance or restraint. He wrought for them in the
way by miracles, he proved and tried them by bringing them into strait places. After the wonderful
dealings of God with them, and their deliverance so
many times, they murmured when tried or proved
by him. Their language was, "Would to God we
had died by the hand of the Lord in the land of
Egypt." They lusted for the leeks and onions there.
. . . Said the angel, "Ye have done worse than
they."— *T., V. I, p. 128.*

*God's Deal-
ing with
Israel.*

1175. How frequently ancient Israel rebelled, and how often they were visited with judgments, and thousands slain, because they would not heed the commands of God who had chosen them! The Israel of God in these last days are in constant danger of mingling with the world, and losing all signs of being the chosen people of God. . . . Shall we provoke him as did ancient Israel? Shall we bring his wrath upon us by departing from him, and mingling with the world and following the abominations of the nations around us? . . . The same injunctions that rested upon ancient Israel rest upon God's people now, to be separate from the world. The great Head of the church has not changed. The experience of Christians in these days is much like the travels of ancient Israel. Please read 1 Corinthians 10, especially from the 6th to the 15th verse: "Now these things were our examples, to the intent we should not lust after evil things, as they also lusted. Neither be ye idolaters, as were some of them; as it is written, The people sat down to eat and drink, and rose up to play. . . . Neither let us tempt Christ, as some of them also tempted, and were destroyed of serpents. Neither murmur ye, as some of them also murmured, and were destroyed of the destroyer."— *T., V. I, p. 283.*

1176. The Lord intends to bring his people back to live upon simple fruits, vegetables, and grains. He led the children of Israel into the wilderness, where they could not get a flesh diet; and he gave them the bread of heaven. "Man did eat angels' food." But they craved the flesh pots of Egypt, and mourned and cried for flesh, notwithstanding the promise of the Lord that if they would submit to his will, he would carry them into the land of Canaan, and establish them there, a pure, holy, happy people, and there should not be a feeble one in all their tribes; for he would take away all sickness from among them.   But although they had a plain "Thus saith the Lord," they mourned and wept, and murmured and complained, until the Lord was wroth with them.   Because they were so determined to have the flesh of dead animals, he gave them the very diet that he had withheld from them.   The Lord would have given them flesh from the first had it been essential to their health; but he had created and redeemed them, and led them the long journey in the wilderness, to educate, discipline, and train them in correct habits.   The Lord understood what influence flesh eating has upon the human system. He would have a people that would, in their physical appearance, bear the divine credentials, notwithstanding their long journey.— *U. T.*, *Nov. 5, 1896.*

1177. The religion of many among us will be the religion of apostate Israel, because they love their own way, and forsake the way of the Lord.— *S. T.*, *Nov. 3, 1890.*

Warnings from the Experience of Israel.

1178. I was shown that the follies of Israel in the days of Samuel will be repeated among the people of God to-day, unless there is greater humility, less confidence in self, and more trust in the Lord God of Israel, the Ruler of the people.— *S. T.*, *Nov. 3, 1890.*

1179. "Moreover, brethren, I would not that ye should be ignorant, how that all our fathers were under the cloud, and all passed through the sea; and were all baptized unto Moses in the cloud and in the sea; and did all eat the same spiritual meat; and did all drink the same spiritual drink; for they drank of that spiritual Rock that followed them : and that Rock was Christ.   But with many of them God was not well pleased : for they were overthrown in the wilderness."   The experience of Israel, referred to in the above words by the apostle, and as recorded in the 105th and 106th psalms, contains lessons of warning that the people of God in these last days especially need to study.   I urge that these chapters be read at least once every week.— *S. T. to B. C. C., p. 43.*

1180 With the history of the children of Israel before us, let us take heed, and not be found committing the same sins, following in the same way of unbelief and rebellion.— *R. and H., 1893, No. 16.*

CHAPTER XLIII.

GOD IN NATURE.

The Source of Power.

1181. Nature is a power, but the God of nature is unlimited in power. His works interpret his character. Those who judge him from his handi-works, and not from the suppositions of great men, will see his presence in everything. They behold his smile in the glad sunshine, and his love and care for man in the rich fields of autumn. Even the adorn-ments of the earth, as seen in the grass of living green, the lovely flowers of every hue, and the lofty and varied trees of the forest, testify to the tender, fatherly care of our God, and to his desire to make his children happy.—*S. of T., 1884, No. 11.*

Object of Education.

1182. The foundation of all right education is a knowledge of God. . . . The first and most im-portant lesson to be impressed upon young minds is the duty of regulating the life by the principles of the word of God. . . . The true object of education is to fit us for this service by developing and bring-ing into active exercise every faculty that we pos-sess.—*S. of T., 1884, No. 12.*

1183. The only safety for the people now is to feel the importance of combining religious culture with general education, that we may escape the curse of unsanctified knowledge. Every effort should be made in the education of youth to impress their minds with the loveliness and power of the truth as it is in Jesus. When the veil shall be removed which separates time from eternity, then will come to many minds the clear perception of the fallacy of human wisdom in comparison with the sure word of prophecy. All true science leads to harmony with and obedience to God.—*U. T.*

**Relation of
Science and
Revelation.**

1184. God is the foundation of everything. All true science is in harmony with his works, all true education leads to obedience to his government. Science opens new wonders to our view; she soars high and explores new depths; but she brings nothing from her research that conflicts with divine revelation. Ignorance may seek to support false views of God by appeals to science; but the book of nature and the written word do not disagree; each sheds light on the other. Rightly understood, they make us acquainted with God and his character by teaching us something of the wise and beneficent laws through which he works. We are thus led to adore his holy name, and to have an intelligent trust in his word.—*S. of T., 1884, No. 12.*

**The Bible
a Test.**

1185. Many, when they find themselves incapable of measuring the Creator and his works by their own imperfect knowledge of science, doubt the existence of God and attribute infinite power to nature. These persons have lost the simplicity of faith, and are removed far from God in mind and spirit. There should be a settled faith in the divinity of God's holy word. The Bible is not to be tested by men's ideas of science, but science is to be brought to the test of this unerring standard. When the Bible makes statements of facts in nature, science may be compared with the written word, and a correct understanding of both will always prove them to be in harmony. One does not contradict the other. All truths, whether in nature or revelation, agree. Scientific research will open to the minds of the really wise, vast fields of thought and information. They will see God in his works, and will praise him. He will be to them first and best, and the mind will be centered upon him.—*S. of T., 1884, No. 11.*

1186. Nature is not God, nor ever was God. God is in nature, the voice of nature testifies of God, but nature is not God. It only bears testimony to God's power as his created works. There is a personal God, the Father ; there is a personal Christ, the Son. —*U. T., July 3, 1898.*

1187. God has permitted a flood of light to be poured upon the world in discoveries in science and art ; but when professedly scientific men lecture and write upon these subjects from a merely human standpoint, they will assuredly come to wrong con clusions. The greatest minds, if not guided by the word of God in their research, become bewildered in their attempts to investigate the relations of science and revelation. The Creator and his works are beyond their comprehension ; and because they cannot explain these by natural laws, Bible history is considered unreliable. Those who doubt the reliability of the records of the Old and New Testaments will be led to go a step farther, and doubt the existence of God ; and then, having let go their anchor, they are left to beat about upon the rocks of infidelity. Moses wrote under the guidance of the Spirit of God,

and a correct theory of geology will never claim discoveries that cannot be reconciled with his statements.   The idea that many stumble over, that God
did not create matter when he brought the world
into existence, limits the power of the Holy One of
Israel.—*S. of T., 1884, No. 11.*

1188. Before the fall of Adam, not a cloud rested
on the minds of our first parents to obscure their
clear perception of the divine character of God.
They were perfectly conformed to the will of God.
A beautiful light, the light of God, surrounded
them.   Nature was their lesson book.   The Lord
instructed them in. regard to the natural world, and
then left with them this open book, that they might
behold beauty in every object upon which their eyes
should rest.   The Lord visited the holy pair, and in
structed them through the works of his hands.

The beauties of nature are an expression of the
love of God for human intelligences, and in the garden of Eden the existence of God was demonstrated
in the objects of nature that surrounded our first parents.   Every tree planted in the garden spoke to
them, saying that the invisible things of God were
clearly seen, being understood by the things which
were made, even his eternal power and Godhead.

But while thus God could be discerned in nature,
this affords no solid argument in favor of a perfect
knowledge of God being revealed in nature to Adam
and his posterity after the fall.   Nature could convey her lessons to man in his innocence ; but sin and
transgression brought a blight upon nature, and in-
tervened between nature and nature's God.   Had
man never disobeyed his Creator, had he remained

in his state of perfect rectitude, he could have understood and known God. But when man disobeyed God, he gave evidence that he believed the words of an apostate rather than the words of God. He was told by the enemy to eat of the tree of knowledge. God had said, "Ye shall not eat of it, . . . lest ye die." But Satan declared that by eating of it man would be exalted to an equality with God.

Adam and Eve listened to the voice of the tempter, and sinned against God. The light, the garments of heavenly innocence, departed from these tried, deceived souls, and in parting with the garments of innocence, they drew about them the dark robes of ignorance of God. The clear and perfect light of innocence which had hitherto surrounded them, had lightened everything which they had approached, but deprived of that heavenly light, the posterity of Adam could no longer trace the character of God in his created works. Therefore, after the fall, nature was not the only teacher of man. In order that the world might not remain in darkness, in eternal, spiritual night, the God of nature must meet man through Jesus Christ. The Son of God came to the world as a revelation of the Father. He was "that true light, which lighteth every man that cometh into the world."

The most difficult and humiliating lesson which man has to learn, if he is kept by the power of God, is his own inefficiency in depending upon human wisdom, and the sure failure of his own efforts to read nature correctly. Sin has obscured his vision, and he cannot interpret nature without placing it above God.— *U. T., July 3, 1898.*

God
at Work.

1189. Many teach that matter possesses vital
power. They hold that certain properties are imparted to matter, and it is then left to act through its
own inherent power; and that the operations of
nature are carried on in harmony with fixed laws,
that God himself cannot interfere with. This is false
science, and is sustained by nothing in the word of
God. Nature is not self-acting; she is the servant
of her Creator. God does not annul his laws nor
work contrary to them; but he is continually using
them as his instruments. Nature testifies of an intelligence, a presence, an active agency, that works
in, and through, and above her laws. There is in
nature the continual working of the Father and the
Son. Said Christ, "My Father worketh hitherto,
and I work."

God has finished his creative work, but his energy
is still exerted in upholding the objects of his creation. It is not because the mechanism that has once
been set in motion continues its work by its own
inherent energy that the pulse beats, and breath follows breath; but every breath, every pulsation of
the heart, is an evidence of the all-pervading care of
Him in whom we live and have our being. It is not
because of inherent power that year by year the earth
produces her bounties, and continues her motion
around the sun The hand of God guides the plan-
ets, and keeps them in position in their orderly
march through the heavens. It is through his power
that vegetation flourishes, that the leaves appear and
the flowers bloom. His word controls the elements,
and by him the valleys are made fruitful. He covers

the heavens with clouds, and prepares rain for the earth; he "maketh grass to grow upon the mountains." "He giveth snow like wool; he scattereth the hoar frost like ashes." "When he uttereth his voice, there is a multitude of waters in the heavens, and he causeth the vapors to ascend from the ends of the earth; he maketh lightnings with rain, and bringeth forth the wind out of his treasures."—*S. of T., 1884, No. 12*

Our Only Security.

1190. All the systems of philosophy devised by men have led to confusion and shame when God has not been recognized and honored. To lose faith in God is terrible. Prosperity cannot be a great blessing to nations or individuals, when once faith in his word is lost. Nothing is truly great but that which is eternal in its tendencies. Truth, justice, mercy, purity, and the love of God are imperishable. When men possess these qualities, they are brought into close relationship to God, and are candidates for the highest exaltation to which the race can aspire. They will disregard human praise, and will be superior to disappointment, weariness, the strife of tongues, and contentions for supremacy.

He whose soul is imbued with the Spirit of God will learn the lesson of confiding trust. Taking the written word as his counselor and guide, he will find in science an aid to understand God, but he will not become exalted till, in his blind self-conceit, he is a fool in his ideas of God.—*S. of T., 1884, No. 11.*

1191. God will not dwell with those who reject his truth; for all who disregard truth dishonor its Author. Of every house that has not Jesus for an abiding guest, he says when he withdraws his presence, "Your house is left unto you desolate." How can those who are destitute of divine enlightenment have correct ideas of God's plans and ways? They either deny him altogether, and ignore his existence, or they circumscribe his power by their own finite, worldly-wise views and opinions. Those who are connected with the infinite God are the only ones who can make a proper use of their knowledge or of the talents entrusted to them by the omniscient Creator. No man can ever truly excel in knowledge and influence unless he is connected with the God of wisdom and power.—*U. T.*

1192. The real evidence of a living God is not merely a theory ; it is the conviction that God has written in our hearts, illuminated and explained by his word. It is the living power in his created works, seen by a sanctified eye. The precious faith inspired of God gives strength and nobility of character. The natural powers are enlarged because of holy obedience. The life which we live by faith on the Son of God is a series of triumphs, not always seen and understood by the interested-parties, but with results reaching far into the future, where we shall see and know as we are known.—*U. T.*

Science Falsely So Called.

1193. Many are so intent upon excluding God from the exercise of sovereign will and power in the established order of the universe, that they demean man, the noblest of his creatures. The theories and speculations of philosophy would make us believe that man has come by slow degrees, not merely from a savage state, but from the very lowest form of the brute creation. They destroy man's dignity because they will not admit God's miraculous power.

God has illuminated the human intellect, and poured a flood of light on the world in the discoveries of art and science. But those who view these from a merely human standpoint will most assuredly come to wrong conclusions. The thorns of error, skepticism, and infidelity are disguised by being covered with the garments of philosophy and science. Satan has devised this ingenious manner of winning the soul away from the living God, away from the truth and religion. He exalts nature above nature's Creator.—*U. T.*

1194. Some may suppose that these grand things in the natural world are God, but they are not God; they but show forth his glory. The ancient philosophers prided themselves upon their superior knowledge. But let us read the inspired apostle's understanding of the matter: "Professing themselves to be wise, they became fools, and changed the glory of the uncorruptible God into an image made like to corruptible man, and to birds, and fourfooted beasts, and creeping things. . . . Who changed the truth of God into a lie, and worshiped and served the creature more than the Creator, who is blessed forever."

In its human wisdom the world knows not God. Its wise men gather an imperfect knowledge of God through his created works, and then in their foolishness exalt nature and the laws of nature above nature's God. Nature is an open book which reveals God. All who are attracted to nature may behold

in it the God that created them.   But those who
have not a knowledge of God, in their acceptance of
the revelation God has made of himself in Christ,
will obtain only an imperfect knowledge of God in
nature.   This knowledge, so far from giving elevated
conceptions of God, so far from elevating the mind,
the soul, the heart, and bringing the whole being into
conformity to the will of God, will make men idolaters.   Professing to be wise, they become as fools.—
U. T., July 3, 1898.

The Infinite God.

1195. Men of the greatest intellect cannot understand the mysteries of Jehovah as revealed in nature.
Divine inspiration asks many questions which the
most profound scholar cannot answer.   These questions were not asked supposing that we could answer
them, but to call our attention to the deep mysteries
of God, and to make men know that their wisdom is
limited, that in the common things of daily life there
are mysteries past the comprehension of finite minds ;
that the judgment and purposes of God are past finding out, his wisdom unsearchable.   If he reveals
himself to man, it is by shrouding himself in the
thick cloud of mystery.   God's purpose is to conceal
more of himself than he makes known to men.
Could men fully understand the ways and works of
God, they would not then believe him to be the infinite one.   He is not to be comprehended by man
in his wisdom, and reasons, and purposes.   "His
ways are past finding out."   His love can never
be explained upon natural principles.   If this could be
done, we would not feel that we could trust him with
the interests of our souls.   Skeptics refuse to believe

because with their finite minds they cannot comprehend the infinite power by which God reveals himself to men. Even the mechanism of the human
body cannot be fully understood; it presents mysteries that baffle the most intelligent. Yet because human science cannot in its research explain the ways
and works of the Creator, men will doubt the existence
of God, and ascribe infinite power to nature. God's
existence, his character, his law, are facts that all
the reasoning of men of the highest attainments cannot controvert. They deny the claims of God and
neglect the interests of their souls, because they cannot understand his ways and works. Yet God is ever
seeking to instruct finite men, that they may exercise
faith in him, and trust themselves wholly in his
hands. Every drop of rain or flake of snow, every
spear of grass, every leaf and flower and shrub,
testifies of God. These little things, so common
around us, teach the lesson that nothing is beneath
the notice of the infinite God, nothing is too small
for his attention.—*U. T.*

1196. "Consider the lilies of the field, how they
grow." The graceful forms and delicate hues of
the plants and flowers may be copied by human
skill; but what touch can impart life to even one
flower or blade of grass? Every wayside blossom
owes its being to the same power that set the starry
worlds on high. Through all created things thrills
one pulse of life from the great heart of God. . . .
He who has given you life, knows your need of food
to sustain it. He who created the body is not un-
mindful of your need of raiment. Will not he who

has bestowed the greater gift, bestow also what is needed to make it complete?—*M. of B.. 136.*

The Mystery of God.

1197. God is to be acknowledged more from what he does not reveal of himself than from that which is open to our limited comprehension. If men could comprehend the unsearchable wisdom of God, and could explain that which he has done or can do, they would no longer reverence him or fear his power. In divine revelation God has given to men mysteries that are incomprehensible, to command their faith. This must be so. If the ways and works of God could be explained by finite minds, he would not stand as supreme. Men may be ever searching, ever inquiring, ever learning, and yet there is an infinity beyond. The light is shining, ever shining with increasing brightness upon our pathway, if we but walk in its divine rays. But there is no darkness so dense, so impenetrable, as that which follows the rejection of Heaven's light, through whatever source it may come.

Can men comprehend God?— No. They may speculate in regard to his way and works, but only as finite beings can.- *U. T.*

1198. Those who think they can obtain a knowledge of God aside from his Representative, whom the word declares is "the express image of his person," will need to become fools in their own estimation before they can be wise. Christ came as a personal Saviour to the world. He represented a personal God. He ascended on high as a personal Saviour, and will come again as he ascended into heaven, a personal Saviour. It is impossible to gain a perfect knowledge of God from nature, for nature itself is imperfect. A curse, a blight, is upon it. Yet the things of nature, marred as they are by the blight of sin, inculcate truths regarding the skilful Master Artist. One omnipotent Power, great in goodness in mercy, and in love, has created the earth, and even in its blighted state much that is beautiful remains. Nature's voice speaks, saying that there is a God back of nature, but it does not, in its imperfections, represent God. Nature cannot reveal the character of God in his moral perfection.— *U. T.. July 3, 1898*

**Beacon
Lights.**

1199. The Bible is the most comprehensive and the most instructive history that men possess. It came fresh from the Fountain of eternal truth ; and a divine hand has preserved its purity through all the ages. Its bright rays shine into the far-distant past, where human research seeks vainly to penetrate. In God's word only we find an authentic account of creation. Here we behold the power that laid the foundation of the earth, and that stretched out the heavens. In this word only can we find a history of our race unsullied by human prejudice or human pride. . . .

In the varied scenes of nature also are lessons of divine wisdom for all who have learned to commune with God. The pages that opened in undimmed brightness to the gaze of the first pair in Eden, bear now a shadow. A blight has fallen upon the fair creation. And yet, wherever we turn are traces of primal loveliness. Wherever we may turn, we hear the voice of God, and behold his handiwork.

From the solemn roll of the deep-toned thunder and old ocean's ceaseless roll, to the glad songs that make the forests vocal with melody, nature's ten thousand voices speak his praise. In earth and air and sky, with their marvelous tint and color, varying in gorgeous contrast or softly blended in harmony, we behold his glory. The everlasting hills tell us of his power. The trees wave their green banners in the sunlight, and point us upward to their Creator. The flowers that gem the earth with their beauty, whisper to us of Eden, and fill us with longings for its unfading loveliness. The living green that carpets the brown earth, tells us of God's care for the humblest of his creatures. The caves of the sea and the depths of the earth reveal his treasures. He who placed the pearls in the ocean, and the amethyst and chrysolite among the rocks, is a lover of the beautiful. The sun rising in the heavens is the representative of him who is the life and light of all that he has made. All the brightness and beauty that adorn the earth and light up the heavens, speak of God.

**An
Unexplored
Field.**

Shall we, in the enjoyment of the gifts, forget the Giver? Let them rather lead us to contemplate his goodness and his love. Let all that is beautiful in our earthly home remind us of the crystal river and green fields, the waving trees and the living fountains, the shining city and the white-robed singers, of our heavenly home,— that world of beauty which no artist can picture, no mortal tongue describe. " Eye hath not seen, nor ear heard, neither have entered

into the heart of man, the things which God hath
prepared for them that love him."

　　To dwell forever in this home of the blest, to bear
in soul, body, and spirit, not the dark traces of sin
and the curse, but the perfect likeness of our Creator,
and through ceaseless ages to advance in wisdom, in
knowledge and holiness, ever exploring new fields of
thought, ever finding new wonders and new glories,
ever increasing in capacity to know and to enjoy
and to love, and knowing that there is still beyond
us joy and love and wisdom infinite,— such is the
object to which the Christian hope is pointing, for
which Christian education is preparing.　To secure
this education, and to aid others to secure it, should
be the object of the Christian's life.— *R. and H.*,
1882, No. 28.

CHAPTER XLIV.

THE SPIRIT-FILLED LIFE.

The Office of the Holy Spirit.

1200. The office of the Holy Spirit is to take the truth from the sacred page, where God has placed it for the benefit of every soul whom he has created, and stamp that truth upon the mind.— *U. T., Feb. 5, 1896.*

1201. The Spirit of God has unconfined range of the heavenly universe; and it is not in the province of finite human minds to limit its power or prescribe its operations.— *R. and H., 1896, No. 34.*

1202. The juices of the vine, ascending from the root, are diffused to the branches, sustaining growth and producing blossoms and fruit. So the life-giving power of the Holy Spirit, proceeding from Christ, and imparted to every disciple, pervades the soul, renews the motives and affections and even the most secret thoughts, and brings forth the precious fruit of holy deeds.— *Sketches from the Life of Paul, p. 131.*

1203. Christ is our advocate, pleading in our behalf. The Spirit pleads within us. Then let us show perfect trust in our Leader, and not inquire of false guides.— *U. T., Oct. 19, 1894.*

1204. The grace of God takes men as they are, and works as an educator, using every principle on which an all-sided education depends. The steady influence of the grace of God trains the soul after

[300]

Christ's methods, and every fierce passion, every defective trait of character, is worked upon the molding influence of the Spirit of Christ, until the man has a new motive power, and becomes filled with the Holy Spirit of God, after the likeness of the divine similitude.— *U. T., March 16, 1896.*

1205. The Holy Spirit is the source of all power, and works as a living, active agent in the new life created in the soul. The Holy Spirit is to be in us a divine indweller.—*R. and H., 1897, No. 26.*

1206. Jesus conveys the circulating vitality of a pure and sanctified Christ-like love through every part of our human nature. When this love is expressed in the character, it reveals to all those with whom we associate that it is possible for God to be formed within, the hope of glory.— *U. T., June 21, 1897.*

1207. Christ is to live in his human agents, and work through their faculties, and act through their capabilities. Their will must be submitted to his will, they must act with his Spirit, that it may be no more they that live, but Christ that liveth in them.— *S. of T., 1892, No. 47.*

1208. Wherever we go, we bear the abiding presence of the One so dear to us: for we abide in Christ by a living faith. He is abiding in our hearts by our individual, appropriating faith. We have the companionship of the divine Jesus, and as we realize his presence, our thoughts are brought into captivity to him. Our experience in divine things will be in proportion to the vividness of our sense of his companionship.—*S of T., 1896, No. 36.*

1209. It is not you that work the Holy Spirit, but the Holy Spirit must work you. There is a winning, compelling power in the gospel of Jesus Christ. It is the Holy Spirit that makes the truth impressive. — *S. T., p. 14.*

1210. To those who truly love God the Holy Spirit will reveal truths that have faded from the mind, and will also reveal truths that are entirely new. — *R. and H., 1897, No. 33.*

1211. Each one must fight his own battle against self. Heed the teachings of the Holy Spirit. If this is done, they will be repeated again and again, until the impressions are, as it were, "lead in the rock forever." — *S. T., No. 7, p. 39.*

1212. As we give ourselves wholly to Christ, our countenances will reflect his image. They will be purified, sanctified, and enobled by his grace. — *U. T., June 27, 1897.*

1213. There is no limit to the usefulness of those who put self to one side, make room for the working of the Holy Spirit upon their hearts, and live lives wholly sanctified to the service of God, enduring the necessary discipline imposed by the Lord without complaining or fainting by the way. — *S. T. on E., p. 120.*

Characteristics of a Surrendered Life.

1214. The whole person is privileged to bear a decided testimony in every line, in feature, in temper, in words, in character, that the service of God is good. — *U. T., Nov. 6, 1897.*

1215. As you surrender to the truth, you will reproduce the truth, a living epistle, known and read of all men. — *U. T., Oct. 27, 1897.*

1216. As God works in the heart, and man sur-
renders his will to God, and co-operates with God,
he works out in the life what God works in by the
Holy Spirit, and there is harmony between the purpose of the heart and the practise of the life.— *S.
of T., 1893, No. 20.*

1217. When Christ comes into the soul, he brings
the calmness of heaven.— *U. T., Oct. 27, 1897.*

1218. The Holy Spirit is his representative, and it
works to effect transformations so wonderful that
angels look upon them with astonishment and joy.—
S. T., May 20, 1896.

1219. When self is merged in Christ, there will be
such a display of his power as will melt and subdue
hearts.— *U. T., April 27, 1898.*

1220. It is the Spirit of God that quickens the
lifeless faculties of the soul to appreciate heavenly
things, and attracts the affections toward God and
the truth. Without the presence of Jesus in the
heart, religious service is only dead, cold formalism.
The longing desire for communion with God soon
ceases when the Spirit of God is grieved from us; but
when Christ is within us the hope of glory, we are
constantly directed to think and act in reference to
the glory of God. The question will arise, "Will
this do honor to Jesus? Will this be approved by
him?"— *R. and H., 1888, No. 16.*

1221. The Bible is full of knowledge, and all who
come to its study with a heart to understand will find
the mind enlarged and the faculties strengthened to
comprehend these precious, far-reaching truths. The
Holy Spirit will impress them upon the mind and
soul.— *S. T. on E., p. 153.*

1222. As the works of God are studied, the Holy Spirit flashes conviction into the mind. It is not the conviction which logical reasoning produces; but unless the mind has become too dark to know God, the eye too dim to see him, the ear too dull to hear his voice, a deeper meaning is grasped, and the sublime, spiritual truths of the written word are impressed on the heart.— *S. T. on E., p. 59.*

1223. If we consent, He can and will so identify himself with our thoughts and aims, so blend our hearts and minds into conformity with his will, that when obeying him, we shall but carry out our own impulses. The will, refined and sanctified, will find its highest delight in doing his service.— *S. of T., 1896, No. 46.*

**Conditions
Favorable to
Growth.**

1224. Real piety begins when all compromise with sin is at an end.— *M. of B., p. 125.*

1225. He who yields himself most unreservedly to the influence of the Holy Spirit is best qualified to do acceptable service for the Master.— *R. and H., 1895, No. 28.*

1226. Your energies are required to co-operate with God. Without this, if it were possible to force upon you with a hundredfold greater intensity the influences of the Spirit of God, it would not make you a Christian, a fit subject for heaven. The stronghold of Satan would not be broken. There must be the willing and the doing on the part of the receiver. There must be an action, represented as coming out from the world and being separate. There must be a doing of the words of Christ. The soul must be emptied of self, that Christ may pour his Spirit into the vacuum. Christ must be chosen as the heavenly guest. The will must be placed on the side of God's will. Then there is a new heart, and new, holy resolves. It is Jesus enthroned in the soul that makes every action easy in his service.— *S. of T.*, *1891*, *No. 8.*

1227. Christians must practise temperance in all things. We have no right to neglect the body and strength and soul and mind, which are to be given to the Lord in consecrated service. We are made up of body and senses, as well as of conscience and affections. Our impulses and passions have their seat in the body; therefore there must be no abuse of any of our organs.— *U. T.*, *Sept. 27, 1896.*

1228. God desires that we shall have a care, a regard, and an appreciation for our bodies,—the temple of the Holy Spirit. He desires that the body shall be kept in the most healthy condition possible, and under the most spiritual influence, that the talents he has given us may be used to render perfect service to him.— *U. T.*, *Sept. 27, 1896.*

1229. He shall shine through their minds as the light of the world. "To as many as received him, to them gave he power to become the sons of God, even to them that believed on his name." But in order that this may be, God demands that every intellectual and physical capability be offered as a consecrated oblation to him.— *U. T.*, *July 6, 1896.*

1230. We are to keep advancing heavenward, developing a solid religious character. The measure of the Holy Spirit we receive will be proportionate to the measure of our desire and faith exercised to get it, and the use we shall make of the light and knowledge that shall be given us. We shall be entrusted with the Holy Spirit according to our capacity to receive it and our ability to impart it to others.— *R. and H., 1896, No. 18.*

1231. The more studiously the intellect is cultivated, the more effectively it can be used in the service of God, if it is placed under the control of his Spirit.—*S. T. on E., p. 57.*

1232. If men will receive the ministration of his Holy Spirit, the richest gift God can bestow, they will impart blessings to all who are connected with them.— *U. T., July 6, 1896.*

Hindrances to Spiritual Growth.

1233. The wilful commission of a known sin silences the witnessing voice of· the Spirit, and separates the soul from God. Jesus cannot abide in the heart that disregards the divine law. God will honor those only who honor him.— *S. of T., 1894, No. 24.*

1234. No one need look upon the sin against the Holy Ghost as something mysterious and indefinable The sin against the Holy Ghost is the sin of persistent refusal to respond to the invitations to repent.— *R. and H., 1897, No. 26.*

1235. Let all examine their own hearts, to see if they are not cherishing that which is a positive injury to them, and in the place of opening the door of the heart to let Jesus, the Sun of Righteousness, in, are complaining of the dearth of the Spirit of God. Let these search for their idols, and cast them out. Let them cut away from every unhealthful indulgence in eating and drinking. Let them bring their daily practise into harmony with nature's laws. By doing, as well as believing, an atmosphere will be created about the soul that will be a savor of life unto life.— *U. T., Aug. 25, 1897.*

1236. God cannot let his Holy Spirit rest upon those who are enfeebling themselves by gluttony.— *R. and H., 1883, No. 19.*

1237. The brain nerves which communicate with the entire system are the only medium through which Heaven can communicate with man, and affect his inmost life. Whatever disturbs the circulation of the electric currents in the nervous system, lessens the strength of the vital powers, and the result is a deadening of the sensibilities of the mind.— *T., V. II, p. 347.*

1238. Why should we not show the attractive part of our faith? Why should we go like a crippled band of mourners, groaning all the way along our journey to our Father's house?— *U. T., Jan. 12, 1898*

APPENDIX

TO

HEALTHFUL LIVING

SUGGESTIVE AND PARALLEL SCRIP-
TURE REFERENCES.

SCRIPTURAL INDEX.

57. Ps. 139:14-16.
58. Ps. 119:92, 93.
59, 60. Rom. 6: 12, 13, 16, 23

CHAPTER V.
Blessings from Obeying Natural Law.

61. Rev. 22:14.
62. Ex. 15:26; Deut. 28:15, 22.
63. Jer. 22:16.
64. Deut. 5:33; Jer. 33:6, 8.
65. Jer. 30:17.
66. Prov. 16:17.
67. Eze. 20:11.
68. Rev. 2:17.
69. 1 Kings 4:34.
70. Jer. 8:13, 15, 22.
71. 2 Cor. 4:11.

CHAPTER VI.
The Consequences of Violating Natural Law.

72. Rom. 1:20-24.
73. Eze. 18:31, 32.
74. Ex. 23:25.
75. Prov. 16:17.
76. Prov. 16:25.
77. Deut. 29:9, 18, 19, 21, 22, 26
78. Rev. 13:16; Gal. 6:7; Rev. 14: 11; Isa. 3:9.
79. Rom. 8:13.
80. Jude 9, 18, 19.
81. Matt. 24:10, 12; Isa. 24:5, 6.

CHAPTER VII.
Natural Law, How Violated.

82. Matt. 12:3-5.
84. Prov. 23:2.
85. 1 Cor. 3:17.
88. 1 Cor. 10:31.
89. Hosea 13:9.
90. Num. 23:19, 20; Col. 2:21.
91. Matt. 25:28.

CHAPTER VIII.
Health.

92. Ps. 42:11.
93. 3 John 1:2.
94. 1 Cor. 6:19.
95. Ps. 40:12.
96. Prov. 4:20-22.
97. Ps. 67:2.
98. Acts 12:8.
99. Prov. 4:23.
101. Ps. 119:92.
102. 1 Cor. 6:20.
103. Prov. 20:29.
104. Prov. 10:27.
105. Jer. 31:33.
106. Jer. 31:29, 30, 34.
107. Isa. 30:20, 21.
108. Ps. 42:11.

CHAPTER IX.
Health Reform.

110. Isa. 58:6-8.
111. Isa. 40:3, 9.
112. 1 Tim. 4:8.
113. Hab. 2:2.
114. Ps. 119:96.
115. Isa. 1:18, 19.
116. Ps. 1:1-3.
117. Matt. 16:24.
118. Rom. 16:17, 18.
119. Ps. 119:96.
120. Deut. 5:32.
121. 1 Cor. 10:7, 11, 31-33.
122. Luke 9:49-56.
123. Luke 17:26-29; Deut. 8:2, 3.
124. John 21:21, 22.
125. John 16:12.
126. Matt. 23:3, 4.
127. 2 Peter 2:21; Luke 12:45, 46.
128. John 1:29; Matt. 3:4
129. Num. 21:5, 8.
130. Eze. 12:18, 23, 25; Titus 2:12, 13
131. Matt. 28:19, 20.
132. 1 John 3:22, 3; 2 Cor. 7:1.
133. Ps. 91:5, 9.
134. Titus 2:12, 13; Matt. 24:48-51

CHAPTER X.

Vital Vigor and Energy.

CHAPTER XI.

Disease and Providence.

CHAPTER XII.

The Influence of Disease upon the Mind and Morals.

353. Isa. 65 : 21.
354. Matt. 5 : 16.
356. Isa. 65 : 2, 4.
360. Lev. 6 : 28 ; Lev. 11 : 29-33.
361. Lev. 3 : 17.
362. John 6 : 12.
364. Josh 9 : 12.
372. Eccl. 10 : 17.
374. Job 20 : 11-15, 21, 23.
378. Prov. 25 : 27.
380. Prov. 23 : 3.
389. Phil. 4 : 19 ; Prov. 17 : 1 ; Prov. 15 : 17.
391. Dan. 1 : 12, 13 ; Eccl. 9 : 7.
394. Ps. 73 : 22.
395. Ps. 145 : 15.
396. Mark 6 : 31.
397. Acts 2 : 46.
399. Prov. 25 : 16.
400. Eccl. 6 : 7.
401. Eccl. 5 : 18, 19 ; Ex. 16 : 18 ; 1 John 3 : 20.
402. Luke 21 : 34.
403. Dan. 10 : 3 ; Acts 9 : 9.
406. Eccl. 10 : 17 ; Ps. 78 : 29-31 ; Luke 21 : 34.
411. Ex. 12 : 9.
413. Num. 11 : 7, 8.
417. Prov. 23 : 3, 8 ; Ps. 141 : 4, 3.
419. Prov. 23 : 6.
421. Luke 17 : 27.
423. Prov. 13 : 25 ; Ps. 36 : 8.
426. Lev. 3 : 17 ; Lev. 17 : 14 ; Deut. 12 : 20-23 ; Lev. 7 : 23, 25, 26.

CHAPTER XIX.
Flesh Foods.

435. Gen. 1 : 29.
436. Ps. 78 : 24-31 ; Ps. 105 : 37 ; Ex. 23 : 25.
437. Isa. 11 : 9 ; 1 Cor. 8 : 13.
438. Gen. 6 : 21 ; Gen. 1 : 29.
439. Rom. 14 : 21.
445. Prov. 23 : 1-3, 6-8 ; Deut. 12 : 20.
447. Jer. 48 : 11.
450. Prov. 23 : 20, 21.
451. Ps. 78 : 31.

453. Eccl. 8 : 11.
456. Gen. 3 : 4 ; Gen. 5 : 5 ; Gen. 5 :27 ; Gen. 6 : 13 ; Gen. 9 : 5 ; Gen. 9 : 29 ; Gen. 35 : 28 ; Gen. 50 : 26 ; 2 Sam. 5 : 4 ; 1 Chron. 29 : 28.
460. Lam. 1 : 13.
463. Ps. 106 : 15.
467. 2 Cor. 4 : 3, 4.
468. Rom. 14 : 21.
472. Lev. 7 : 15, 16, 17 ; Ex. 12 : 9.
474. Lev. 19 : 6, 7.
476. Isa. 65 : 2, 4 ; Isa. 66 : 17.
477. Ps. 106 : 28, 29 ; Ps. 91 : 9, 10.
480. Num. 11 : 5, 6 ; Isa. 19 : 8, 10 ; Hos. 4 : 3.

CHAPTER XX.
Stimulants.

482. Eph. 5 : 18 ; Deut. 29 : 18-20.
483. Isa. 28 : 7.
484. Prov. 10 : 27.
485. Prov. 31 : 4-6.
491. Prov. 4 : 19, 17.
492. Ps. 119 : 73, 92, 96, 67.
503. Deut. 5 : 9.
504. Isa. 28 : 7, 8 ; Deut. 21 : 20.
505. Col. 2 : 21.
506. Hosea 4 : 10, 11.
507. Prov. 23 : 30-32.
508. Deut. 32 : 32, 33 ; Num. 6 : 3 ; Mal. 1 : 7, 12 ; Lev. 10 : 9.
511. Prov. 20 : 1 ; Eze. 44 : 21.
512. Isa. 5 : 11, 12 ; Rom. 13 : 12, 13.
513. Prov. 31 : 5.
514. Rom. 14 : 21.
515. Prov. 23 : 29, 30 ; 1 Cor. 6 : 10.
516. Eph. 5 : 18 ; 1 Cor. 6 : 19, 20.

CHAPTER XXI.
Dress.

521. Matt. 12 : 30 ; 2 Cor. 3 : 2, 3.
522. Prov. 3 : 5 ; Ps. 139 : 14 ; Gen. 1 : 27.
523. Titus 2 : 4, 5 ; 1 Tim. 2 : 9, 10.
524. John 21 : 7 ; Ex. 28 : 2, 3 ; Matt. 22 : 11 ; Matt. 3 : 4.

CHAPTER XXXIII.

Moral Maladies.

923. Gen. 4 : 5, 7 ; Gen. 6 : 2, 5.
924. 1 Cor. 6 : 13, 15, 16, 18.
925. Ps. 58 : 3.
926. Prov. 22 : 6.
927. Matt. 24 : 37-39.
928 and 929. Ps. 69 : 22.
930. Eze. 16 : 49.
931. Prov. 18 : 9 ; Prov. 21 : 25.
932. Prov. 6 : 16, 18.
933. Prov. 13 : 20.
934. Ps. 36 : 4.
935. Matt. 18 : 14.
936. Eze. 16 : 26, 27.
937. Deut. 6 : 6-12.
938. Prov. 3 : 13, 16, 22-24
939. 1 Cor. 6 : 13.
944. Prov. 20 : 11.
947. Rom. 1 : 28.
949. 2 Tim. 3 : 2.
950. Eze. 16 : 49 ; Isa. 3 : 9 ; Prov
29 : 1 ; Rev. 22 : 11.

CHAPTER XXXIV.

Rational Remedies for Disease.

951. Job 12 : 7-10.
955. Eze. 18 : 22.
961. Prov. 5 : 15.
962. Ps. 104 : 10, 11 ; Ex. 23 : 25 ; Dan.
1 : 12 ; Neh. 9 : 20.
964. Isa. 44 : 12.
966. Num. 19 : 7 ; Isa. 1 : 16.
967. Jer. 2 : 7, 22.
968. Lev. 15 : 1-13.
973. Neh. 9 : 20 ; Isa. 55 : 1.
976. Gen. 18 : 4 ; Eze. 16 : 4.
977. Job 9 : 30, 31.
978. Mal. 4 : 2.
979. Eccl. 11 : 7.
981. Lev. 14 : 34-48.
982. Matt. 4 : 16.
983. Deut. 33 : 13, 14.
984. Isa. 1 : 5, 6.

985. Isa. 26 : 3.
986. Rom. 8 : 6.
987. 2 Cor. 4 : 4.
988. Prov. 16 : 24 ; Phil. 4 : 7.
989. Isa. 64 : 7.
990. Rom. 12 : 2.
996. Prov. 15 : 16 ; Prov. 16 : 3.
997. Prov. 12 : 25.
998. Lam. 2 : 11.
1000. Neh. 2 : 2 ; Prov. 15 : 13.
1001. Prov. 17 : 22.
1002. Isa. 58 : 7, 8.
1003. Job 22 : 21.
1004. 1 John 3 : 21.
1005. Isa. 58 : 8.
1006. Prov. 10 : 22.
1007. Mal. 4 : 2 ; Isa. 40 : 31.
1008. Matt. 8 : 16.
1011. Prov. 14 : 8, 12, 27.
1012. Isa. 20 : 3, 4.
1013. Job 22 : 7, 9, 10, 21.
1014. Ps. 103 : 2, 4 ; Ps. 27 : 1, 2.

CHAPTER XXXV.

Prayer for the Sick.

1015. Prov. 28 : 9.
1016. Ex. 15 : 26 ; Deut. 7 : 12-15 ;
1 John 5 : 14, 15.
1017. Isa. 55 : 7 ; Ps. 66 : 18.
1018. Prov. 28 : 9.
1019. Gen. 4 : 7.
1020. Ps. 119 : 67, 71, 92.
1021. Mal. 3 : 10.
1022. Ps. 103 : 3 ; Matt. 9 : 2 ; Isa. 1 : 5.
1023. Prov. 28 : 13.
1024. Deut. 28 : 58-61.
1025. Deut. 29 : 9 ; James 2 . 7.
1026. Joshua 7 : 10, 13.
1027. Rev. 14 : 13.
1028. Prov. 3 : 6 ; Matt. 26 : 39.
1029. Ps. 91 : 9, 10 ; James 5 : 13-16.
1030. Ps. 142 : 4, 5.
1031. Ps. 118 : 17, 18.
1032. Hosea 6 : 1 ; John 11 : 44.

1033 John 5:6, 7; Matt. 15:27, 28.
1034. Luke 18:1.
1035. 2 Kings 20:7; Isa. 38:5.
1036. John 9:31.
1037. Isa. 63:9; Ps. 147:3; Isa. 61:
    1; Luke 12:6.

CHAPTER XXXVI.
Drugs.

1038. Ps. 103:3, 4.
1053. Jer. 30:12-14, 17
1056. Mark 5:26.

CHAPTER XXXVII.
The Missionary Nurse.

1061. Luke 10:9.
1063. 1 Cor. 12:9.
1065. Ps. 127:2.
1068. Gen. 21:17, 18.

CHAPTER XXXVIII.
Medical Students.

1070. Col. 4:14.
1071. Luke 10:9.
1072. Matt. 4:23, 24; Luke 9:11.
1073. Luke 10:30, 33, 34, 37.
1075. Deut. 15:11; Matt. 24:6, 7.
1076. Hosea 4:6, 10, 11.
1077. Jer. 8:22.
1079. Rom. 12:1.
1080. Mark 5:26.
1081. Isa. 64:7-9; Job 6:14.
1082. Matt. 20:34; Isa. 63:9.
1083. Acts 10:34.
1084. Prov. 3:1-35.
1085. Rom. 1:21, 22, 28.
1086. Dan. 1:8, 10, 19, 20.
1087. Ps. 119:130.
1088. Ps. 27:11, 12.
1089. Eph. 6:13.
1090. Prov. 13:1.

1091. Prov. 3:11, 13, 21-23, 32; Prov.
    4:5-13, 21, 22; Eccl. 9:10.
1092. Matt. 5:14, 16; 1 Chron. 12:32.

CHAPTER XXXIX.
The Missionary Physician.

1094. John 15:20.
1096. Rom. 12:1.
1097 and 1098. Eph. 6:11, 13.
1099. Ps. 119:10, 14.
1103. Mark 10:49.
1104. Matt. 25:40.
1105. Mark 5:26.
1108. Matt. 9:12.
1109. Job 6:21.
1110. Job 13:4.
1111. Job 16:2-5.
1112. Col. 2:3.
1113. Lev. 5:17.
1114. Prov. 13:13-15, 17.
1116. 1 Cor. 9:25.
1119. Matt. 9:12.
1124. 2 Tim. 2:24-26.
1126. Jer. 8:22.
1127. John 12:32.
1128. Eze. 14:23; 2 Tim. 2:19, 21.
1129. 1 John 2:6.
1130. Eze. 20:11; Deut. 6:24.
1131. 2 Tim. 4:2.
1132. Isa. 13:12.
1134. Eph. 6:7; John 17:15.

CHAPTER XL.
Medical Missionary Work.

1135. Matt. 10:7, 8; Luke 10:9.
1136. Matt. 21:31; Luke 14:21, 23.
1137. Mark 3:14, 15.
1138. Ps. 41:1-3.
1139. Mark 3:14, 15.
1140. Deut. 28:1, 10, 13.
1141. Luke 10:8, 9.
1142. Hosea 4:6.

1143. Isa. 60 : 2, 3.
1145. Luke 19 : 10.
1146. Isa. 40 : 3 ; John 1 : 29 ; Matt.
      9 : 35, 36.

CHAPTER XLI.
Christian Help Work.

1147. Ps. 41 : 1-3.
1148. John 19 : 26, 27.
1149. Luke 14 : 23.
1150. Eccl. 11 : 1, 6 ; Acts 20 : 20.
1151. John 14 : 6 ; 1 Cor. 1 : 29 ; 1 Cor.
      12 : 7.
1152. Isa. 61 : 1-3 ; Heb. 2 : 17, 18 ;
      Luke 19 : 10 ; Rom. 12 : 14.
1153. Isa. 63 : 9.
1154. Prov. 28 : 27 ; Acts 20 : 35.
1155. Isa. 58 : 6, 7.
1156. 1 John 3 : 17 ; Job 29 : 16.
1157. Amos 5 : 11 ; Prov. 19 : 17.
1158. Ps. 140 : 12 ; Phil. 2 : 15.
1159. Eze. 34 : 3-6.
1160. Isa. 40 : 1 ; Heb. 1 : 14 ; Ps.
      34 : 7.
1161. Matt. 25 : 35-40 ; Matt. 10 : 42 ;
      Acts 10 : 38 ; 1 Peter 2 : 21.
1162. Deut. 15 : 7-11.
1163. Mark 16 : 17, 18.
1164. Isa. 58 : 7 ; Ps. 68 : 6.
1165. James 1 : 27 ; Acts 9 : 39.
1166. Ps. 68 : 6 ; Isa. 58 : 7 ; Job 29 :
      12 ; Matt. 5 : 46 ; Rom. 15 : 1.
1167. Ps. 126 : 6 ; Eccl. 11 : 1 ; Job
      29 : 13.
1168. Prov. 11 : 25, 26 ; Isa. 33 : 15, 17.

CHAPTER XLII.
Lessons from the Experience of the Children of Israel.

1169. 1 Cor. 10 : 11 ; Deut. 28 : 1, 15, 22.
1170. Num. 16 : 2, 3, 13, 14.
1171. Amos 8 : 11.
1172. Deut. 30 : 19, 20.

1173. Num. 21 : 5 ; Ex. 16 : 3, 4 ;
      1 Cor. 10 : 11.
1174. Num. 11 : 4, 6.
1175. Ps. 78 : 24-31 ; Titus 2 : 12-14 ;
      Ps. 105 : 37 ; Ex. 23 : 25.
1176. Ex. 15 : 26 ; Deut. 12 : 20, 23.
1177. Ex. 16 : 3.
1180. Zeph. 3 : 13.

CHAPTER XLIII.
God in Nature.

1181. Rom. 1 : 20.
1182. Ps. 111 : 10.
1183. Isa. 30 : 20, 21.
1184. Ps. 19 : 7.
1185. Matt. 24 : 35.
1186. Heb. 1 : 1-3.
1187. Rom. 1 : 21, 22.
1188. Gen. 2 : 8, 9 ; Ps. 19 : 1 ; John
      15 : 5.
1189. Ps. 107 : 21-43 ; Heb. 1 : 3 ; Ps.
      147 : 8, 16 ; Ps. 135 : 7.
1190. 2 Cor. 4 : 3, 4, 6, 16, 18.
1191. Prov. 1 : 7 ; Prov. 8 : 13.
1192. Rom. 8 : 16 ; John 3 : 16 ; Isa.
      40 : 26.
1193. Prov. 4 : 19.
1194. Rom. 3 : 1, 2.
1195. Ps. 139 : 1-17.
1196. Jer. 33 : 20, 21 ;. Matt. 6 : 28-30.
1197. 1 Cor. 16 : 25-27 ; Isa. 40 : 12-18,
      21-24.
1198. Acts 4 : 12.
1199. 1 John 3 : 2.

CHAPTER XLIV.
The Spirit-Filled Life.

1200. Eph. 3 : 16, 17.
1201. Ps. 139 : 7-10.
1202. John 15 : 5.
1203. 1 Thess. 5 : 19 ; Rom. 8 : 26.
1204. 1 Thess. 5 : 23 ; 1 Cor. 6 : 11.
1205. John 14 : 16, 17.
1206. Rom. 5 : 5.
1207. Gal. 2 : 20 ; 2 Cor. 6 : 16.

CLASSIFIED INDEX.

GENERAL INDEX.

[331]